MW00844462

Animal Hotel

Also by Diana Cooper

YOU'LL NEVER BE BORED

Animal Hotel

DIANA COOPER

St. Martin's Press
New York

ISBN 0-312-03782-1

First published in Great Britain by Michael Joseph Limited.

First U.S. Edition

10 9 8 7 6 5 4 3 2 1

To Pa

Animal Hotel

I

"Come this way," I suggested, "and I'll show you the, er, arrangements."

I was aware it sounded a bit coy, like conducting a modest visitor to the loo, but "I'll show you the Kennels" had a dire ring about it, like viewing the condemned cell. The sealyham already looked anxious enough.

It was a lovely afternoon in early summer. Away to the west, the fields ran downhill towards a reservoir which crinkled in the mild breeze like crumpled foil. Pink roses scrambled over the old house and the daisies beyond were like drops of milk on a green cloth. Away and below moved the motorway, a panoramic hymn to instability.

My first boarder looked as if it had just walked out of the pages of a Dornford Yates novel, together with an owner who was also very much in character. They had arrived the day after my small ad. appeared in the local paper – which was much too soon after I moved into the house and while I was still wondering where I packed the teapot.

"I'm Bella Farringdon," said my first customer. She paused. I had an uneasy feeling she expected me to recognise the name, so I said "Of course!" quite heartily as if I did. She went on: "I read your advertisement and wondered if I could come over and look at your facilities." We all know about the milkman's testimonials, but what had I to offer? So far there were just three bowls marked DOG and a crate of 'Barkerbeef (For Your Friendly Pet)' and that was all. Well, apart from those grim timber kennels which looked for all the world like a canine concentration camp.

I had really expected people to ring up and make bookings for future dates, the way one writes off on Boxing Day to get a place on a package tour for late September. Then I would have had time to encourage the roses to curl round kennel doors perhaps, or hang lace curtains, and add winsome names like "Bide-a-Wee" on the gates. But here was a lady on the doorstep and sounding very determined.

I said she could, of course, see whatever she liked, any time at all, threw the front door open wide, stood back and let her get the full impact of unpacked tea chests in the wide hallway where coloured glass from the double doors threw shades of purple, wine and gold all over the faded floorboards.

Bellas are usually buxom and this one was no exception. The dog was much the same. She told me it was a miniature and this was confirmed by neat paws and ears, but elsewhere it was tubbily overweight. They were both spotlessly clean and well-groomed. Both had bright eyes and sharp clear voices. Both smelled of Chanel No. 5. The dog had a blue collar with rhinestones and the mistress a white collar with pearls. One could have seen both of them as cuddlesome. Plump, fluffy bitches have an appeal most people find irresistible and I would go along with that myself. But I could see the whole project being ruined if I started cuddling the customers.

I used a warm, benevolent smile from a collection I always have ready, and tried not to coo like a demented dove over Bustle. She was clutched under Bella's arm and kept looking from her to me in an appealing way that was at once anxious and eager. I set off to lead the three of us round the stable wall only to be faced rather abruptly by the kennels in all their stark emptiness and disinfected immaculation. The bolts, bars and padlocks were quite a shock after the honeysuckle arch and mellow weathered brickwork behind us. It was a solemn reminder of life in a Siberian salt mine, Dartmoor prison on a wet February evening or a holiday camp I once saw on the East Coast during a depression. I led them straight past at a firm trot.

"There," I announced when it was out of sight, and with a dramatic gesture to cover my uneasiness "is the Exercise Meadow." I pointed towards an area of soft, Cumberland turf. "The dogs come out here to romp in the sunshine."

It sounded quite idyllic, though the idea had been born of instant necessity to show her Something Favourable, and it did seem to have promise. I hoped there wasn't a snag, but we could only find out about that when the dogs got inside – and then probably got out, indicating a need for better fencing. But there were certainly advantages, with me idling away the summer under a spreading chestnut tree, with a selection of books and long, cool drinks, supervising from afar happy boarders bounding and bouncing in eternal joy. A metaphorical wide-brimmed hat I keep ready for just such occasions came to the fore.

"And where would Bustle sleep?" asked Bella warily, her eyes roaming the playground for signs of pending danger.

"Well," I countered, just as warily, "where does Bustle *usually* sleep?" I couldn't risk losing my first customer.

"On my bed, of course." She looked surprised I could ask such a stupid question. I was prepared for 'in her basket' and already had in mind the small spare-room, but before I could stop myself I was saying, "Then that's where she'll sleep while she's here! On mine . . ." I gave a weak laugh, hiding from myself the horror of what I was doing, but Bella was being ecstatic with gratitude and relief. I mentally put up the weekly fees. Oh, well, I comforted myself, she's not that big. It's long-legged breeds you have to watch if you don't want a paw up your nose in the middle of the night.

"And does Bustle have her own basket?" I went on bravely, thinking I might just get her off and under eventually. But Bella was clutching my arm and gushing, "It's *so* marvellous to have found you! I can leave her now with every confidence. I'm going to Cannes with a friend, you see, and we always sleep together . . ."

I felt sure she was talking about the dog.

". . . so I must be sure she's going to be happy. I'll come home at once if she frets, of course. I'm so relieved you can take her. It's just the sort of place I'd choose and you're so kind, so dedicated." I tried to look the part, modestly smirking. "But I was so afraid you'd be full up."

If Bella had been anyone else, the remark might have been sarcastic. We were, after all, walking past acres of empty kennelling which didn't exactly give the impression of being sizzling busy. A calm silence, unbroken by even an occasional bark, hung over the afternoon. On an impulse I admitted, "You're my first customer. I only put the ad. in this week. I moved in here on Tuesday. My husband's in hospital and I can't even find the teapot yet. But I promise you I'll cherish Bustle. I've kept dogs all my life and I've three of my own in the kitchen. I could never have too many around." I'm no clairvoyant, so at that moment I really meant it.

The day we first went to see the derelict old house set in five acres close to the motorway from London to the coast, I said, "I'll be able to run boarding kennels!" with just the same enthusiasm I once said, elsewhere, "I'll market lilies!" and at other times, in other places, "I'll have a herb farm!" "Sell tomatoes" "Cultivate peaches for local hotels" and so on, through other people's leftover lives and hobbies, which I could see at once being turned to my advantage. It meant the spadework was done, and I liked that. I'd sooner turn a hemmed curtain into a caftan than buy 5 metres and start from stage 1, "pin your pattern". So if someone had already dug the foundations, it seemed simple commonsense to grab the opportunity, work my way up, and tile the metaphorical roof. Then I could just take over and enjoy the profits.

Not that profits always followed, of course, but one could try. I had once heard my husband comment to a friend that if we ever went to jail, I would somehow find a way to take in prisoners and charge them bed and breakfast; and in the unlikely event of him taking Holy Orders, I would stand by the font and charge for hassocks. It isn't that I'm commercially inclined, but I am unable to miss an opportunity, which this time happened to be kennels, iron-railed with heavily swinging iron entrance gates. Timber constructions, with runs and gates into an exercise yard. High brick walls round the grounds to keep in the most monstrous of wolfhounds. All I had to do was move in, put out the news that dogs were welcome, order a crate of Shapes, get friendly with the butcher and I was in business. It had to be more successful than herbs, anyway. All that seeding, feeding and weeding, only to end drying, tying, some of them dying and nobody buying had taught me nothing but to shudder at stuffing.

I tried to sell lilies for funerals before Death began to take over from Sex as the Brave New Subject to be fearlessly tackled by the media on every topical programme and in every chat column, and everyone who wasn't joining in and snuffing it, rushed to get in on the act of Undertaking. But Death just wasn't the trendy thing to do by the time my lilies were posing their waxen faces at financial angles under plastic covers. The Big Boys were at it with their fibreglass flowers ("Make a Save On the Grave") and the real thing was out. Even the local florist told me rather rudely that my packer was a rotten bruiser. As I was grower, salesman, accountant, as well as lowly cutter, weeder and packer, I was suitably indignant. "It's the mourners, you see," he explained when he saw my expression. "Gives 'em a bad name. Everyone can see I had to knock a bit off."

Tomatoes hadn't been much better. I only had two greenhouses, neither of them heated, and no forcing sheds, so my tomatoes were ready at the same time as every cottage was boasting great clusters of their own ripe fruit hanging scarlet and luscious in windows and on garden walls. Shop prices were so low by then that I didn't even cover the cost of fertiliser, and we all got pink-eye through a diet consisting mainly of pips in the plectrum or something.

And that brings me to the ambitions I had of being a fruit farmer. We had taken over a discarded convent with a large orchard, obviously used mainly as an object lesson for rejecting temptation, as the trees themselves were terribly neglected. At the same time I happened to buy Lot 88 at an auction which I thought was going to be "Set of Saddle Clips and Veil", but turned out to be "Box of Books and Political Pamphlets". It was a mistake anybody could have made. The pamphlets were all in German or I might have become Prime Minister, and most of the books were incomprehensible, except for something entitled *Fruit Farming Made Easy*. No wonder it went for my ridiculous bid which I only made in the first place out of curiosity about the saddle clips. However, you do get these signs from above and, coupled with the large orchard we were about to inherit, how could I take it but as a broad hint? I'm simple enough to believe anything, God knows. In fact, it seems God knows that very well so maybe it was a bit unfair, but once I had admired the colour plates of Granny Smith it seemed dead easy to sit back during the winter with Chapters 1 to 12, burning old apple logs and eating Golden Delicious: I would then watch the bridal blossom burst into summer from my leisurely seat under the lilacs, and eventually rouse myself to pick the luscious fruit, skipping lightly from tree to tree wearing that wide-brimmed hat and laughing roguishly over my shoulder at some lissom lover leaping from behind the Bramleys during hazy days of fruitfulness.

So I sat back all winter, growing too fat for any skipping and leaping and thus repelling lovers for the rest of the year. Come spring and there was nothing on the trees except squabbly starlings. The snowdrift of white blossom I had in mind for early summer was only happening down the road at Peel and Core Ltd. (Amalgamated Fruit Farmers).

I did lose a few pounds fretting about my commercial future and then decided there was nothing for it but to ring Mr Peel and introduce myself. I tried to sound as if I wouldn't be averse to a little light dalliance when the sukebind was on the wane and a little less on the hips. Always providing, of course, that my trees were heavy with ripening Russets – so what could he advise with that end in view?

There's nothing a professional hates more than showing off the bit of knowledge *you* need. They'll show off anything else to the point of tedium. Never that. It's like demanding an opinion on your impacted wisdom, indicating it with a cherry stick at somebody's cocktail party.

Mr Peel asked what sprays I used. It could, of course, have been a cautious preliminary to possible dalliance, but I took it he wasn't referring to hair or deodorant. Just bark and branch. I wasn't using any, so I made non-commital noises, tried out my throaty laugh (which sounds as if I'm under ten stone) and we went on to pruning. I hadn't done any of that either. I was beginning to see there was more to it all than I thought. He seemed worried about my claim to have pruned "here and there", "now and then", by which I really meant snapping off a twig in passing. He could see I was taking too much for granted, I think, and he asked if I wanted his honest opinion.

I don't like honest opinions. No one ever offered an honest

opinion that made me feel any good. Why is honesty always so unpleasant when it concerns advice? Why doesn't anyone ever say, "If you want my honest opinion, you've nothing to worry about" and if you have got something to worry about why don't they say, instead, "This is going to make you feel awful but it might help." Only they don't. Anyway I did what I always do and clamoured, foolishly, for his honesty as if I enjoy being knocked flat by a professional using his diploma rolled up as a baton. I decided long ago that honesty is often nothing less than a pseudonym for revenge.

Mr Peel said he could recommend only one thing to save my orchard. It might be too late for this season but it was worth a try. I listened with pencil poised and breath bated.

"Gentleman's dung," he said firmly. "That's what your trees need. Gentleman's dung." And he rang off.

I never did know whether it was just a polite way of saying what he thought of me for cadging advice free of charge. And I never tried it. I wasn't sure I knew any gentlemen but even if I could somehow sort out a few, surely they'd be the very ones to avoid discussion on the proposition? You don't do a dung deal with *gentlemen*. And over an acre or two it would have needed such a lot. So I put away the wide-brimmed hat, borrowed an electric saw and did quite well with apple logs delivered free during the autumn.

Dogs seemed altogether a more viable possibility. They don't need packing or pruning or spraying or fertilising – or if they do, they manage it for themselves. Anyway, I like dogs and I can't say I was ever mad about lilies or mint.

So here I was, optimistic as ever and with Bella thrusting Bustle from her cushiony bosom into my inadequate, half-empty shirt. I staggered a little. Bustle weighed as much as a child of four. I wasn't sure whether this was a demonstration of trust or merely that Bella's arms ached. But as I felt Bustle snuffle up to me – all that warm fur, those brown eyes, even the Chanel No. 5 – I knew with a sinking heart that I'd never be able to lead any dog from its owner to those cheerless kennels. Come four or forty, I'd feel bound to share hearth and home and even bed if that's what they were used to.

Luckily, of course, some of them weren't. They were the bigger ones – well, some of the bigger ones, and even then . . . The trouble was that the idea sort of caught on, grew to be expected, was finally accepted, and there were eventually times when I dreaded having to fight to get a space for sleep myself. But in the weeks following Bustle's takeover bid for the eiderdown, boxes and baskets were brought along with blankets, balls and bones and within no time at all I was filling corners and cupboards all over the house. And the occupants *still* followed me upstairs at bedtime.

It reminded me of a previous house we had lived in, on the Cornish coast. It overlooked a wide blue bay and every summer we were crowded to the attics with visitors. Not that they all followed me upstairs at bedtime – they were usually far too involved in gin rummy, love affairs, Scrabble, eating or arguments. We were tremendously popular. Friends we hadn't seen or heard from for years; people we'd only met once; acquaintances of people we ourselves could scarcely remember from way back; even people who arrived saying they thought we were other people and stayed on to find how wrong they were. They lay on *our* beach, made love in *our* beds, ate everything in *our* deep freeze, borrowed and broke *our* tennis racquets, used *our* bikinis, underwear, overcoats and money, and then went back home with a tan, two dozen fresh eggs and a pound of clotted cream. Ah! if only I'd cashed in on *that* opportunity! Instead, I was always left with a pile of laundry, an empty fridge, and a box of Black Magic pressed into my hand with an invitation to drop in and stay at their basement flat in Fulham any time I might be passing. I daresay it was the memory of those unrewarding summers that started off the whole vehicle of ventures which followed.

But dogs are different from people. They don't eat your stuffed marrow and then lean back and begin to tell you the right way to do it "for next time". They don't snooze in the bath, sleep on the sofa, read in the loo or smoke in bed – and if they do, they can be shouted at without creating an atmosphere at the breakfast table. The only things I could be sure about at this point, however, was that dogs don't suck lemons, don't help themselves to the sherry, and have a convenient way of staying quite still on the floor so that you can step over (and even on) them without causing trouble. They also occupy the best chairs so that I have to sit on the floor when I want a good cry or to get my wellies off. But visitors do that too. I also knew I loved dogs, cats and small scuttling mice, that I was never lonely or bored in their company, and would have been miserable without them. And I couldn't say that about visitors.

Bella Farringdon's visit ended with us both sitting on upturned crates drinking mugs of coffee. She completely dropped her earlier attitude of ingenue playing a grande dame. She relaxed, we giggled together, exchanged confidences and became friends. She offered to tell my fortune in tea leaves, but though I had a quarter of Orange Pekoe Tips, I still couldn't find the teapot, and anyway I wasn't sure I wanted to know the future before I had to.

She confessed she was going on holiday with somebody else's

husband, and admitted a fear that he might get cold feet. It seemed to me the least of her worries and I said so.

"Oh, I'll be keeping the rest warm," she assured me. But if they did have to come home before the time was up, she offered to come over and lend a hand till she had to go back to work.

I said rather quickly that I hoped her holiday would last as long as she wanted it to and she mustn't think of spoiling it by coming back early. If he did lose his nerve, he would just have to let her stay on there at his expense, it was the least he could do. There were lots of other smashing husbands to meet in a place like that. I knew she was going to have a really wonderful time. My goodness, I did. We hardly needed tea leaves to tell us that! Truth was, I just couldn't see her Chanel No. 5 mixing with the Shapes.

And so she came back a day or two later to leave Bustle, the blanket, ball and brushes. A tiny one for teeth, a "tootsy" brush for toes and a real bristle hairbrush for the coat. For me she brought a frilly white organdie blouse which wouldn't meet over her 38″ and wrapped twice round my 34. It was quite difficult to get her to go, and she kept saying part of her longed to stay on with me, Bustle and the Boys, as she would call my three bitches. I watched her go with relief.

Bustle and I sat and stared at one another. She accepted a small bit of my mid-morning biscuit, then she spread out in the sun, head on front paws, and fell asleep. My own bitches Mattie, Rosie and Treacle lay nearby, accustomed to sharing me amongst themselves, willing to welcome all comers so long as they knew their basket and left individual bones alone. I glanced round at work waiting to be done, strewn straw packing, old newspapers from boxes of china, coffee stains on the bare table and I wished I could go to sleep as well.

But then the phone began to ring and it was the hospital.

2

We had been living in Kent when the coronary, with complications, disrupted what, in any case, threatened to be a thoroughly exhausting move up country. They rushed my husband out of the crates and cardboard boxes and into the peace of an intensive care unit. I was left with a straw-strewn floor, seven pieces of my Winter Woodland dinner service in pieces where the stretcher bearers had trampled, and advice to be at the hospital "as much as possible in case we need you for signing things". Not in case he took a turn for the worse which was of obviously lesser importance.

There was no question of postponing the move, as other moves were rarin' to go in a chain reaction ending up with us. Nowadays, it only takes a mild case of flu for some people lacking a conscience to devastate whole areas of civilisation.

I couldn't help thinking it seemed a bit coincidental my husband chose that moment to get wheeled away. I'm not saying he fixed the whole thing, mark you, but it does seem odd that he happened to get sent to America just before the previous move and that he never got in on the hassle of the one before that because of sneezing. He thought it was the straw the men used for packing, though I can well remember hay never made him sneeze in our courting days. He sneezed for three hours almost non-stop and had to go to Casualty for treatment where they advised him to keep well away from the action. He's never had a good sneeze since.

Then there was the time he lifted a tea-chest so I could start loading saucepans or something and ricked his neck. An elbow one could understand, even a disc, but the neck demanded a plaster collar and as much rest as possible to get over the shock. There wasn't much rest among rolled-up carpets and the accumulated dust of ages. So he went off to stay with friends in Bude and the shock was all mine. No, I mean it's just a coincidence, that's all.

But it does mean I'm quite good at staggering round with wardrobes and coping with the cat who always shoots up the first new chimney, pretending terror. Everybody knows she only does it to get the sardines we have to use to tempt her down. This time I put the cat in the bathroom, where she leapt into the bath, knocking the shower tap and then yowling as her long black tail caught the sudden downpour. When I rushed back in to save her, she shot past me through the door, swearing loudly, and dived over the bedroom balcony rails, by great luck clutching the clothes line on her way down. After that I didn't see her for a couple of days and then, just when I'd given up all hope, she meandered in, swishing her tail and dropping a dead mouse disdainfully in my slippers.

These are minor things that happen during anybody's move, I know, but why is it I'm always the one to have to remove the mouse?

The trouble was I learnt so little from experience. For instance, in any move one should watch out for pilfering. Pilfering in removals is never petty. You don't notice a missing fish slice or a nylon toothbrush. And if you happen to have accumulated a houseful of stuff, it's quite on the cards you wouldn't even miss a silver salver till Christmas. You can even persuade yourself a three-piece suite must be in the roofspace waiting for the carpet to be laid in the sitting-room. Removal men do funny things like that. They take fancies, as well as objects.

I was once very surprised to see an escritoire exactly like the one I inherited from my grandmother, for sale in the window of a local antique shop a week or two after the move was over. I hurried back home, uneasily trying to convince myself I only wanted to compare the two, but actually trying to rack my brains and recall where the removal men, in their infinite taste, had seen fit to place it. Well, they had quite obviously seen fit to place it with the local antique dealer, but it had all been done so neatly and with such planning and forethought that it was impossible to prove it was mine and illegally come (or gone) by. After all, they said, I had never reported it, had I? And the foreman said he'd never seen an escritoire in the van.

One firm to whom I wailed a list of losses simply said, "Look, lady, who do you suppose would take on such a bloody awful job without the perks?" He made me feel a downright heel for being so small-minded.

In the end, I gave up driving myself mad to make sure the teaspoons arrived, or the corner cupboard with 1696 carved on a Victorian panel (probably in 1937) still concealed some illicit love letters in its secret drawer, and wrote all losses off to charity.

Now, as the telephone rang among the tea chests, the old resentment at standing single-handed against the rising tide of problems, threatened to get me. I knew it would be my husband. No one else had the number. He had a room to himself and the occasional use of a telephone on a trolley, and he was certainly over the worst.

He was, of course, using his suffering voice, and I was using my hearty one. The chasm had begun to grow between us because neither side, for different reasons, could act naturally. We were moving separately through different worlds of worry and it's too easy for clasped hands to lose contact across the great divide.

Pa croaked wearily, "Hullo, darling. How's it all going?" and coughed. The cough was a reminder that he was the only man in the world who could have developed a barking coronary.

"Fine, fine. Everything's fine," I said, with forced cheer. "The teapot went missing, but as it's chipped I doubt if it'll find its way to the Victoria and Albert Museum." The line crackled over his answer, so I went on, "Every moment reminds me of Move Four!" which was the one where he tripped over the saucepans and cut his eye on – would you believe? – a piece of folded newspaper? Two days at the eye hospital and two weeks recuperating with friends, I think it was that time. We went on playing the game of Competitive Courage with subtlety and undertones that might have promoted either of us into the Diplomatic Service. We both privately considered the other had the best of an unequal partnership.

Pa always managed to get his Disaster well in advance of any I might have in mind to forestall events, such as breaking my neck or going mad with beriberi and into immediate isolation. Grimly, on Move Four, I went ahead and moved us all into a pleasant Victorian mansion with innumerable wings and towers and turrets, and among the woodworm and wireworm I found an elderly couple still occupying a few assorted rooms in the rafters. Both were nudging eighty. So, having left the eye-patch and white-stick in Wales, I was only to find myself into Geriatrics. I felt ambushed, I can tell you.

The couple had been cook and gardener to a previous owner who inconsiderately died suddenly and left them with nowhere to go. They were extremely apologetic, deaf as wooden Indians and yet surprisingly active. Once I had shouted soothing noises to reassure them I wasn't going to call out the Guard, they became extremely docile and eager to help. They stayed on for nearly a year and did all my cooking, a lot of my gardening, crotcheted innumerable antimacassars (which I still use as dinner mats) and polished shoes, cars, the lawn-mower and even handles on garden tools, mainly because they enjoyed being occupied where the family was. I never felt so cherished in my life and when their son found them a small cottage near his own home, we parted in genuine and mutual tears of regret.

My husband said he felt fine, just fine now. Well, better, anyway. Not himself, of course, not yet, but, well, fine. Everyone was very kind. People in hospital always say everyone is very kind as if they go in expecting to be beaten up by a posse of Sisters. He said they were looking after him with every possible care. I said he was jolly lucky. I said it with feeling. Then I relented a bit and told him about Bella and Bustle and the strange disappearance of Mr Treddie, the decorator who had promised to welcome us with fresh paint and clean rooms. I suggested that we may have employed a Do-It-Yourself company, as the place was full of ladders but empty of men with paint-pots.

I could tell he wasn't really interested, because he said "Lovely" in the way one does to a child moaning on about Billy Wilson's bike, so I said rather sharply that I couldn't visit him, of course, but I'd keep writing and we could phone one another, and he wasn't to worry. Whatever he did, he really mustn't worry about me. I'd get by somehow. Didn't I always muddle through? He said, with some feeling at last, that he could agree there. As for the visiting, he said I wasn't to worry about that. Quiet and freedom from anxiety were essential in his state. Anyway, it would be very unwise to go gadding about because the valuables left behind would be available for marauders. He lives in a dream world that a painting he picked up at a bazaar is really a lost Turner, and a set of chairs I bought at an auction for £5, with accidentally collapsible legs, to be Chippendale. He checks that both treasures are still there every time a visitor leaves.

When I put down the phone, I began to feel lonely. I almost hoped for a resident ghost. The house was early Victorian, a good period for spooking which goes well with wide, sweeping staircases, and high, hollow ceilings. The best thing about it was the view. In every move we made, views abounded. Oceans and mountains and rolling acres of forest, but for me nothing compared to this. They had all been beautiful, but still. This one moved. This one was peppered with small bright colours which glowed like shooting stars at night or humming-birds during the sunlight hours, shimmering up and down the long ribbon lying below. The Motorway.

I felt like stout Cortez, "silent, upon a peak in Darien". A pity the lines always give me the picture of some fat gentleman standing gleefully upon a small, angry dog, because I know a little of what Mr Cortez and his men must have felt in their first realisation of a new land. I am in some danger of developing a fixation on motorways. They enchant me. I once found a huge colourplate of some new arrangement to by-pass and cross-partition a Midland city, had it reproduced to poster size and framed, and visitors are much more inclined to gaze at it, riveted with interest, than even to glance at the "lost Turner".

So feeling lonely, I rang my friend Marsha. I had to tell somebody how I felt. Marsha lives in London with Timmy, her cat. Husbands have come and gone but Timmy stays, a tribute to constancy and the attributes of cods' heads. One in-between lover had told Marsha that only instant impotence could result from any of her saucepans, so she was usually out, eating at Ali's, King Ho's or Dave's Dive. Today, luckily, she was in, working on one of her cosmic cushions. Marsha worked the most unbelievable designs on velvet with paint, beads and dead flowers, which she sold easily and profitably for love notions. A nap with one's head on the cushion and one could be assured of waking either randy as hell or cured of insatiable passion. It was all one to Marsha. She said the whole secret was more in the incantations stuffed inside with the foam rubber chips, but customers liked to see something they couldn't understand. I had one of the cushions myself, but apart from a strong smell of fish, nothing special had emanated from it for me over the years. I was still hoping to use it to get a response from someone else when the opportunity arose.

"Hi! Marsha," I said eagerly. "I'm here!" I could hear a wailing violin in the background and the occasional clash of cymbals.

"Darling, lovely. And I'm here . . ." It had to mean something.

"I mean, I've moved in. You know, up here, off the Motorway. It's so beautiful, you'd adore it. You could use all the shapes and planes and . . ."

"*So* allergic to aircraft," she muttered, as the cymbal was dropped on the bare floor and rolled under the sideboard.

"That's not the radio, is it?" But she didn't go in for contemporary magic.

"It's Fraction. A new group I'm helping. Fraction in Action, two violins and a . . ." She tailed off.

I said, "It's under the sideboard." The violins wailed higher. I added in a shout, "I'll ring you again when you're free," and put down the phone. Marsha wouldn't mind. She wouldn't notice. Funny how two people, poles apart, me practical and her so mystical, could maintain a lasting friendship and understanding. My husband had once said we were Witch and Bitch, but that was after we ganged up to reject his claim that a small worn rug bought in the local jumble sale was Aubusson.

The removal men had obviously sorted out the few items of any interest to them and left the rest to me. Over the years I had grown to like the haphazard results of their attention to detail and usually left everything where it was for a while. After all, the nature of my husband's work meant that they would probably be back to collect it all again in a few years. I noticed the sitting-room carpet was now in the spare room and it wasn't a bad idea as the bed could stand over the worn patch. The rug used to hide the worn patch could now stay where it was, in front of the kitchen range. The old rug once used in the kitchen would be good enough for the conservatory so that dogs could lie in the sun there and enjoy watching birds on the lawn. The dining-room carpet was rolled up, fretfully shedding its fringe in the hall. Laid flat, it could stay there and cover the oak-strip floor and save polishing. In moving, you often find a natural sequence of distribution you might never have considered otherwise.

Outside the sun was flicking its fingers at me through the branches of a narrow prunus. The house could wait. I had to inspect the business premises. If the kennels were to be my income, they were more important than Gracious Living.

The wooden sleeping quarters were damp and smelly, unused for years. The roofs opened from the top as well as having a front entrance, so with some difficulty I raised them all to the sun and fresh air and wished one could do the same with a house. I sat on top of the Sick Bay and made notes. Inside the hut was an electric power point, a sink, a bench with cupboards above, and a calendar for 1969 showing two dogs dressed as a Come Dancing couple doing the tango.

There were twelve single kennels, four double ones and three smaller boxed-in areas which must have been for suspected rabies or virulent puppy-pox. There was a general Exercise Yard as well as individual runs to each kennel and everywhere sloped to excellent drainage.

They were less vulnerable than lily-beds, more valuable than coriander and basil. I told myself that this time I was on to a jolly good thing. The motorway led to the coast, and the coast had hotels where dogs were not welcome. They could refer dog-despairing customers to me. Dogs would be dropped in on the way and collected again going home. Why, I thought, with great cunning, I might suggest the owners popping over now and then during the holiday and whisking off old Smudgey for a romp on the Prom. I was staggered at my luck: stunned by my opportunities. But how on earth was I going to cope with the hordes of dogs seething up the motorway and turning off at Junction 7, all eager to get in on the act?

The rush seemed to have begun, because something was coming up the drive. I jumped down from the Sick Bay roof, smoothed my hair, and walked forward wearing my welcome smile.

It was the post van. I kept the smile going because postmen are important in a rural community: you can stand or fall by your postman's report. I waited for him to join me and then held out my hand and we exchanged introductions. The postman said his name was Humphrey.

"Not a very big boarding kennels, was it?" I commented, already planning extensions on all sides. Humphrey rested his satchel on the car radiator and made a great show of sorting the mail to find something for me. He had one eye which could only be plastic because it never moved, though the other spun about at twice the normal rate to compensate – or show off, the way a kid with normal legs does in front of one with calipers. The plastic eye seemed to be considering my cleavage without much enthusiasm. I shifted bare feet and wished I were better dressed for the occasion. At one time, a school had owned the property. Then a retired Army officer. So until I came along, everything was neat and tidy.

"Boarding kennels? Major Forster didn't board, he bred."

"Oh," I said, flattened. The plastic eye moved away as he bent his head inside his jacket to shelter the light for a fag-end. I watched nervously. I felt any accidental conflagration would be made a lot worse by the inflammable eye. My father once caught fire to his wallet that way.

When we were safe again, I asked, "Bred what?"

"Dogs." He sent a stream of smoke across his face and I watched the one good eye flicker and close. An impressive trick wasted on me by then. Humphrey had too much else going for him. Local knowledge, for instance. "Yes," he repeated, "it were dogs he bred, dogs."

It seemed an unlikely place for rabbits or racehorses. "What kind of dogs?"

"Them messy things. Don't know what you call 'em – know what I call 'em though! Messy things. You gotta spanner?"

I was carrying nails to fix some wire netting where it had come adrift. "In the house," I said. "What size do you want?"

"Not me, miss! The wife'd never hear of it! We 'ad a moggy once and that weren't too bad but it got run over by Uncle's invalid carriage and upset 'is suspension. No, miss, we don't want no more."

I should have guessed he meant spaniels. He went on. "Anyway, I were bit by a spanner up Rowanditch way. Got me right in the . . ."

". . . shall be boarding all breeds," I interrupted firmly. "Small in the house and bigger ones out here, of course." I was delighted to hear myself solve the space problem so easily, so I repeated it to make sure I got it right. "That's it. Little ones indoors and the bigger fellers outside." I tried not to look smug but it really was a marvellous idea. If I could just bring myself to *do* it . . .

"I'm going to contact hotels off the motorway so that guests going there on holiday can leave their dogs with me. I'll notify the airport too" (a brilliant afterthought) "and I'll suggest people can fetch their pets for the day whenever they like and bring them back after tea."

Humphrey and I stared at one another in shared surprise.

"Runs along the cliff-top, gambols on the beach . . ." I went on, happily.

"Dogs on beaches shouldn't be allowed," said Humphrey with disapproval "All them turds . . ."

I broke in hastily, "Well, over the fields then, wild and free." I was already seeing it in terms of advertising copy.

"Running wild encourages them to mangle sheep," he finished darkly.

"Well," I protested, knowing how weak I sounded, "I think it's a terrific idea. It's what everyone wants, surely."

But Humphrey didn't want it. My good ideas were a feeble challenge to his sinister mangling. He went on, "A doddle for some!"

I suppose he meant me, picking up the cash, but I immediately saw further publicity on hoardings just beyond the roundabout: "LEAVE YOUR DOG AT THE DODDLE. A HOLIDAY HOME FROM HOME. A BONE-US FOR BONZO!" It's an opportunity I'm very glad I missed. Anyway, the house was inaccurately called The Hollies.

Humphrey got back in his little van, said goodbye and weaved away, steering with one eye on the road. I was left congratulating myself on hitting the jackpot at last, but wondering how a successful business would affect the rates. Euphoria is a state controlled by the Borough Treasurer, and I felt sure that even as the ambulance had trilled away, Pa had been heard to mutter "The rates, my God, the rates!"

It has always been tacitly understood that whatever my current venture, profits would somehow pay the rates and sometimes it worked out. After all, my personal expenditure was miniscule. A working wife is not so much a joint provider as a limited spender. If you're occupied elsewhere, you can't get to the sales, the auctions, Pippa Dee Parties or the cinema. You can't be risking your all at bingo, charity bazaars, on the golf course or with lovers in Bath teashops. A man's motto should be, "A working wife is a *safe* wife". Wives who work outside the home rarely get time to look at glossy magazines or yearn noisily after Acapulco. And they're too occupied climbing their own particular rainbow with their mixed company, to concern themselves with what might be going on in anyone else's.

I rang the decorators again in the afternoon, using a cool air of detachment to show how little their inefficiency bothered me. This was because once they became brisk and busy, bills would follow automatically, and those did bother me.

"Mr Treddie?" I enquired with a bright smile at the telephone. It was Smile 1 in my repertoire, Forced and Fixed. "I notice you don't appear to have begun the work here as promised."

"Beg pardon?" he demanded in the tone of someone begging for nothing but your immediate return to sanity. "You will have noticed our ladders I think?" He spoke as if they completed the matter.

"Well, yes," I agreed, "but . . ."

"And we did, I think, say 'soonest possible' in my epistle?"

It was possible he had a copy in front of him. I didn't.

I sighed. "The fact remains, Mr Treddie, that you don't seem to have begun on the work and we have now moved in. Taken possession. Occupied the premises. I can't possibly have your men here now, so I think we had better postpone plans for the time being altogether." I switched to Smile 3, Triumph, and sat back. I believe one must keep smiling, not for any Pollyanna reasons, but because smiling keeps one's facial muscles exercised the right way. It also keeps spectacles from slipping off the end of one's nose and drives everybody else mad. It helps one concentrate on what's happening (which is almost always funny one way or another) instead of what's threatening (which often isn't). I run a series of smiles and most of them are now subconsciously numbered and filed away in my head. A touch of the mental computer and we're away – foe daunted.

"I seee," murmured Mr Treddie, lingering on the word to let me know he could see, indeed, right through my little scheme to cancel his absurd estimate, and was preparing to cross me off his visiting list altogether in future. "My chaps are a bit tied up as it happens. A Council job: emergency case of flush fittings." Put that way it sounded like plumbing, urgent. What he really meant were the built-in wardrobes on Council estates put his way by brother-in-law Councillor X. The local paper had, I noticed, a few banner headlines about cost to ratepayers of under-floor heating adjustments, electronic self-opening garage doors to replace manual up-and-overs (now obsolete) and it seemed quite possible they could have decided to rush in emergency window seats for all I knew. Instant Fitments are a byword on rate-controlled homesteads.

I sighed "The rates, my God, the rates!" and he said, "You'll be letting us know, then?" and we both silently debated whether or not we really needed the work after all, and where would the money be coming from.

No one can compete with the sort of largesse handed out liberally by Councillor Midas, City Treasurer.

On the other hand it was no good telling myself the house wasn't too bad. The walls were standing and might even take enough pictures to cover the worst bits, but the paintwork looked as if a thousand mice had been after the lead. Maybe it could all wait till I'd made enough from my customers to pay the bill? Maybe I could do it myself? I kept quiet about the ladders in the drawing-room – after all, they might come in handy. We exchanged civil goodbyes and I put down the phone and picked up the Yellow Pages. I'm sure Charles Forte never stopped to whitewash a wall before getting down to build an empire.

The power of the Local Press may not be in the same class as that of the Nationals, but it's a hell of a lot cheaper. Like the house that Jack built, I had to get the boarders to pay the bills to buy the paint to do the walls to save the cash to pay the rates to live in the house I'd chosen: and for that chain reaction, the first link was advertising.

3

I drove into the nearest town the following morning. It was seven miles away and began cautiously with a few large Victorian houses, hiding modestly behind skirts of suitable trees. Then the road suddenly widened out past the Public Library and ran straight into a market square surrounded by supermarkets, traffic lights and a daunting threat of double yellow lines. There was a grave shortage of parking space and the two areas boasted by the Council on large signs only proved to be full up when I finally found them. In the end, and after circling the entire town twice via one-way streets and eager traffic wardens, I drove away on the coast road and found a small open space where a row of cottages had been demolished and where a group of other cars were obviously being parked off the road by conscientious shoppers.

It was a long walk back into the High Street where I had to find the offices of the local paper, so I left a bundle of cleaning in the car for another time.

It's always best to be wary of grey-haired ladies behind piles of forms. The odds are that they've been there a long time together, and the ladies have become bossy with boredom. You play it with authority, but kindly and with caution.

I said chattily, "*Good* morning! *Such* a shortage of car parks in the town! Next time it might be better to come by helicopter and see what it's like on top of the Town Hall!" As a resident, she immediately took any criticism as a personal affront. There was no hint of a smile, though I paused to give her the chance for a work-out on it. I could see only business would win her round, so I said hastily, "I would like to put something in your Classifieds."

It sounded like a veiled threat but she indicated a shuffle of papers with a movement of her head and there was a swing of her ear lobes where dangling gems in the pierced flesh pulled them out of orbit. I took a form and found it carefully lined with a little box at the far end. I had already worked out a rather catchy heading and the pithy details to follow. Taking a ballpoint from an old yoghurt carton, I began: "AND HOW ABOUT OLD REX THEN? You're off to have a funtime: is he to be left with unwilling friends? reluctant relatives? Let him have a holiday, too! Good company, super food, own bed, daily games, log fires. Special diets catered for. Medication on hand . . ." and ran right off the edge of the form and over the little box (which I planned to leave blank for maximum publicity until I saw it was for the number of words used). However, I added up, put my phone number and pushed back the lot over the counter.

The grey-haired swinger read it through with growing dismay. Then she, too, counted the words. She wrote something across the top of the paper which might have been "DANGEROUS LUNATIC" and then asked, "Do you want HOLIDAYS or PERSONAL?" and added that it would be £4.96 as it was the very limit.

So, I decided, was the cost. I took back the form and screwed it up. Then, as she watched, I took another and wrote "HOLIDAY HOME FOR DOGS" and my phone number. I was working out a rough estimate of 5p a word, maybe 8p even 10p and at that rate, this entry could go in several different columns and catch the maximum number of eyes. It didn't sound so good, of course (I'd quite fancied such a holiday as the original wording myself, and I could see she had) but it was probably a more commercial venture into public relations.

She said it would be £1.50, that being their minimum charge although I had used less than the number allowed and it was in advance, please.

I took back the form, blushing a bit, and threw that one aside, too. Then I took a third, read the instructions on the reverse side, and began again: "HOW ABOUT OLD REX THEN? Holiday Home for Dogs" and my phone number. She kept me waiting a full minute as a punishment, so I put her pen in my pocket. The fact that she asked for it back as I reached the door later did nothing for my morale.

Meantime she was suggesting I put it under HOLIDAYS as well, for an extra 69p, where it would be listed with Hotels and catch the eye of people planning to go away. I thought that reasonable enough and gave her another pound, and while she was fishing about under the desk for change, she asked, "Do you take cats?"

She was still cross about something and it sounded as if she suspected me of being a drug addict. You never know what they're going to call the stuff next. But I said, "No, only dogs at the moment, though I hope to expand later," which was another possibility only occurring to me as I said it, even if it did sound like a supermarket manager considering a department for wines and spirits.

She said she had a cat. Fusty, she added, and he only had false teeth. She thought his sight was going too. I said maybe he needed glasses as well, but she gave me another cold look and I suddenly realised she said "four teeth" not false. The trouble with moving a lot, of course, is dialects. I never quite catch up and in the past I often found that as soon as the family were acquiring a West Country burr and merging nicely, we were off again and they had to start all over with an East Anglian slurr. All dialects are suspect to other dialects and maybe if we all stuck to one there would be a lot less prejudice about. For myself, I found it easiest to maintain a South London prim and be considered snobby. I still longed for an interpreter sometimes.

I thought she might know more about local facilities than most, and began to ask her things like where was the best vet? the cheapest pet shop? and where I could find the best bones. She might have said "the cemetery" and we could have had a bit of a laugh but she was fed up with me and pretended she had no idea where anything like that was. I bet Fusty ate finely-cooked fish. She said she would get a frame put round my insertion, which sounded pretty enough in its way, but unfortunately cost extra. And before I had time to take back the form a fourth time (now marked FRAME by her in heavy black capitals) she said it worked out at £3.71 and would I please hand over the rest. She didn't say why it was such an odd amount but she had me thoroughly cowed. Maybe she was adding the cost of Fusty's supper. I said I'd keep in touch for repeats and she said in that case I'd better fill in a blue form, too.

But I really had got myself involved far enough. I muttered about catching a bus and fled.

The next call would have to be the vet. I had turned up several addresses in the Yellow Pages before leaving home and I chose Mr Lamb because he sounded less aggressive than Mr Battle and more reliable than Mr Stagger. A Mr Lamb would be prepared to use good, old-fashioned methods like Epsom Salts and Stockholm Tar, not the newer things which work out at £5.35 for every injection in a course of six while you know full well that a good dose of Turkey Rhubarb from behind the compost heap would have been just as effective and much quicker.

I trudged back to the place where I'd left the car. There was a man standing looking at it. Mine is an unpretentious little job. It doesn't assume originality, it doesn't arouse envy, it doesn't stir a crowd to silent admiration, cost a fortune to insure, nor make the neighbours feel inferior. No one has ever desperately wanted my little car but me. And I don't even desperately want it myself any more. I just find it useful when it eventually starts. It does do that at regular intervals if you know how to threaten it.

I couldn't think what the man staring at it could see in it, except a bundle of curtains for the cleaners rolled up on the back seat, several plastic carriers for the shopping, a rake with the head off for clouting baleful hitch-hikers, and Pa's trilby with a hole in the crown where he once caught a stray lead pellet at a rectory tea party by standing with a girl called Brenda behind the rifle range. It caused a lot of comment at the time, not entirely about the risk of rifle ranges, either. He swears that hat saved his life, if not his reputation. I keep the hat in the car to remind him about Brenda. You can do with any amount of things like that in a marriage.

"Hullo," I said to the man, brightly, in order to disarm any attempt at daylight robbery. "Nice day." I was flattered he found my car worthy of attention. I unlocked the door and got inside. I was smiling No. 6, Disarming.

"Just sold it," he said. He sounded smug.

"Sold what?"

"This 'ere car."

Smile No. 6 vanished. I said, "What on earth are you talking about? It's *my* car. I only left it here half an hour ago."

"So it sold quick," he agreed. "Some do."

What was this? Someone to whom we owed cash? There were quite a few of those. Why else was I about to embark on the greatest money-spinner of all time? The countrywide network of Dogs' Holiday Homes which would become as famous as Butlins – and not al that different.

I said coldly, "Is there a car park attendant around? If not, please get out of my way or I'll call the police."

It didn't cut any ice. He gave me a long straight stare of honest reproach. Then he grinned – a bastard version of my No. 3 – Triumph. That's why I like to keep them listed, you recognise what's going on behind the expression.

"Lady," he said with patient resignation, "you think this 'ere's a car park, don't you? It ain't. It's Joe's Dump. There's a sign . . ." He pointed to the far end. I'd driven in from the other side where a row of posts had been roughly uprooted.

"So?" I queried uneasily. I wasn't too sure of my ground now knew it was also Joe's.

"Joe lets anything go for twenty nicker. I mind it. What I mak over the top's me own. I got a bit more on yours."

I wasn't in a mood to be flattered. The other cars were a bit roug but mine had optional extras. Like curtains to be cleaned and a ha with a hole in it to remind us of Brenda.

"There's been a hilarious mistake!" I laughed, wondering ho our devious laws – which turn a man's castle into anybody's onc he's left for the Crusades – would regard a Morris Minor left empt on someone else's dump.

" 'e's coming with a tow."

"He'll be lucky to have both legs if he tries to take my car," I said grimly, starting the engine. The man took it quite well. He sighed.

"Right," he said, "if you 'ave to take that hattitood . . ." he paused. "I'll settle for a fiver," and he came over and leered menacingly through the window, putting one hand on the steering-wheel.

"Don't be ridiculous," I said. "You could see all this stuff in the back and you knew perfectly well it was here by mistake, not dumped on Joe. Now do go away!" and I let in the clutch. His hand was still on the wheel. I wrenched the car to turn, speeded up and he fell behind me. In my mirror, I saw him flat on his back. I shot out into the traffic and straight into the lane of an oncoming bus. The driver bawled something obscene which I deserved, so I gave him my No. 2, Dazzle, and drove like the clappers away from the town centre, back towards the hinterland.

I was terrified both he and the man in the dump yard had the car's number, would track me down, sue me, smite me, report me, strangle me or set the dogs on me. I decided to quit town until the heat was off. And I didn't stop until I was a good mile from the Town Hall – and it was then I remembered my purse. I don't carry a handbag. They look dotty with Levi's and cowboy boots. At one time I considered stuffing everything into a horse's nosebag which would, at least, have blended, but in the end I decided to make do with large pockets for combs and lipsticks, lists and library cards. I guess cowboys do the same, or maybe they stuff wallets in their boots and that's why they walk funny. I've never found a place for my purse so it's usually in my hand and now it wasn't. Now both my hands were trembling so much that my little finger kept nudging the indicator.

I checked the front seat, back seat, the map shelf, glove compartment and door pocket.

I then remembered I was sitting on my purse for safety. I drew to the side of the road and stopped. I repeated fourteen lines of Tennyson's *Princess* which usually calm me, though I'm not sure what they're all about, and then looked round to see where I was. I could have been anywhere on earth. The road was the kind you get leading out of every country town: large Victorian houses with creeper, front gardens with privet, coloured glass in front doors, and modest gables. You can almost see the aura of boiled cabbage and polished lino.

I was still a bit shaky and kept peering over my shoulder. I have this horror of being followed. The car used to have a faulty spring in the boot which often sprang open when least expected. It happened the first time while I was out driving in a busy main road and I thought I could see a large lorry right in behind me, clinging to my bumper. I speeded up a bit to get ahead of it, but the bastard hung on, always right up there in my rear window. I tell you, I got really mad. In the end I was so absorbed in trying to shake it off that I shot some traffic lights on the change and got hauled over by a passing constable.

I explained about the lorry, which had vanished suddenly, somehow leaving my boot lid open. The copper suggested a breath test. Of course, on Instant Coffee it merely turned the nozzle brown, so he let me off. He just thought I was one of those weirdos who get chased by flying saucers.

But no one was creeping up on me, like Sylvester's puddy-tat, so I shut my eyes again and indulged in another few lines of Tennyson, only to find that some of the words escaped me, which just shows the state I was in. I usually know yards and yards of it. Poetry, specially the old meandering kind, makes a very practical and cheap tranquiliser. Less time-consuming than meditation, which I always think is OK for maharishas, fakirs and soul singers who don't do much work, but not for me. Like the rest of the rabble, there's only time for a quick Keats while I clean the bath or de-louse the dog.

When I opened my eyes again I felt a lot better. I could see two huge stone gateposts which heralded a large house behind them, and boasted a doctor's brass plate on one side, nicely polished. Once or twice I'd wondered about registering with a doctor. This was a good moment to go in and sign on, find out where I was and begin having a worry about something else. Doctors and dentists always find something wrong so that they can fill it up on a claim form. The doctor might even ask me in and offer something to allay my present stress – such as a martini with ice and lemon. They have claim forms for them, too.

I checked in my mirror, tidied my hair, smiled 0.5 (Lukewarm) and stood in the sunshine next to a late forsythia peering round the posts. The name on the brass plate was Hebditch. Oh dear, I thought, he'll be middle-aged and grey all over. Surnames are almost as revealing as first names. You know where you are with a Harry or a Julian. Tough/Sensitive. But with a surname, it's even worse in a way. The origins of all names lie in ancestral skills or habitat, and a Hebditch would, I supposed, be one who at some time hebbed ditches. I'm not sure what hebbing is, but it's almost sure to be boring and dull and would have printed its characteristics on descendants for ever.

The church clock was hovering at the midday hour. The doctor might, of course, be out on his rounds, in which case Mrs Doctor would see me reluctantly, with half her mind on the kitchen. I'd have to add an extra layer of charm to the smile I used in supermarket queues when I have to write a cheque and hold up a line of impatient cash customers. I also had a bar of nut milk in my pocket and that would help. Doctors' ladies are seething volcanoes under their own layer of soothing charm. They seethe because they're the ones who have to lose sleep and beauty early in the cause of pregnant schoolgirls. They go for comfort in caramels or gin.

She opened the door. I could see at a glance she was gin. Not to excess, but with vermouth and high heels. I pushed the chocolate deeper back into my pocket and sought other tactics. She wore one of her husband's white coats and one of her own pink scarves. No woman of her calibre would have a husband who wore anything like that.

I extravagantly admired the forsythia. I practically raved about it. I felt sure she gardened. Doctors' wives get savage with secateurs while the casserole cools and the water dries up round the plum duff. Then I noticed she had lilac finger-nails and capped teeth and I finished with the forsythia rather abruptly and said, "Is the doctor in?"

She said, "This is the vet's". I'd only checked on the name, not the profession. But isn't that just what I'd been looking for?

"Heck," I murmured reverently. "Isn't that incredible? It could have been a dentist's! A vet's just what I need . . ."

She looked at me closely, suspecting an advanced case of mange.

"Is he at home, then, *Mr* Hebditch?" Never mind the name. Mr Lamb would have been meek and mild which isn't much good with a case of rabies. Now, if he'd only been Mr Shepherd – but on second thoughts, hebbing sounded like a worthy skill, requiring perseverance, patience and tenacity. He'd do.

The lady gave a hollow laugh. "Home?" she repeated. "He's never home."

If I hadn't known quite a lot of professional wives – I mean wives of professional men – I would have thought Mr H. had left her and could be found in a block of discreet flats having it off with a veterinary student over advice on Forty Ways to Fetlock or something. His wife went on, "I'm lucky if we have breakfast together these days." I was surprised. Her hair was a commercial for conditioners and I would have said she'd have every earnest young student outstripped, stripped out, any time.

Inside the house, looking past her, I could see it was clean, late Victorian, but furnished in sheer but careful Casual, which showed a hint of Scandinavia with strong overtones of real comfort. For instance, there was no lino, but good brown carpet squares. Surgery on the ground floor with dispensary and waiting-room. Sitting-room, inconvenient kitchen, office on the first. Bedrooms above, three at the most. I said sympathetically, "I know how it is, pastry ruined, potatoes mushy and Yorkshire Pudding flat."

She said, shortly, "It's salad, limp. He's on a diet."

Usually when a woman says anything about a diet to me, I'm always coping with one, too, or say I am. People get obsessed about diets, to the point where any other subject only hints of strawberry waffle meringue. And if she says her husband is the one on a diet, then I say mine is, too. If she said he was on a monocycle tour of Greenland, a Scouse bender, one leg or a hatstand in the hall, I'd find a point of equation. A woman with a husband of any kind needs all the understanding she can get and if he just happens to be on some side kick as well, then, like as not, she'll be looking to you for support. A diet shared isn't exactly a diet halved, I've found, but if you're both on the same endurance trip, it's a bit like being hit by the same bomb and sets up an immediate relationship. So I said, "So is mine! Well, most of the time, anyway. We do lapse into sausages . . ."

She said, "*I* don't diet," rather wearily as if she was sick of the subject. I said admiringly, "*You* don't have to. Anyone can see that. I don't have to either because I fidget." If you notice, fidgeters are never overweight. It's easier than counting calories.

I thought we needed a more positive line of action so I said I'd give her husband a ring during the evening. I only wanted a chat, I assured her, and I turned to go. She said in measured tones, "Business, I suppose?" sounding very hostile, as if the word 'funny' ought to have come first, so I stopped. I realised my hair was too pink, due to over-enthusiasm with the cochineal which I thought might make me a strawberry blonde but merely looked as if my scalp was blushing, or I was in for a nasty attack of herpes. Maybe she thought I was a retired go-go dancer who'd unfortunately gone-gone a bit too far. Maybe she thought I'd called round trying to drum up interest in getting a fourth abortion for her Pekinese, Siamese or even herself. Or I might have been a lady hoping for a bust. I always have been.

I did once know a dentist, not doing too well, who had to give up sideline abortions when they went on the Rates, and turned his hand instead to boobs and nose jobs. He gave silicone injections to increase the size and shape of anything, either sex. He became very popular and ran a Merc and a Mini with black windows until he met this stripper, who wasn't doing too well either. He fell in love with the fantastic figure he created, but was tormented by the fact that it was really more his than hers, like Gainsborough having a yen for his Blue Boy, and grew insanely jealous of what she did with it. He finally shot himself, but she never knew about that because she'd taken an overdose when an oil sheikh offered her a job as Head Girl in his harem if she'd just slim a bit because he liked boyish figures. On second thoughts, I think that must have been a story I read in a flight magazine on the way to Holland. They do like to rivet your mind completely to keep it off the odd loose wing or lurking terrorist. But real life isn't all that different. I did actually know a girl called Mistletoe who asked for a larger bust and a smaller nose on the National Health, please, but there was such a lot of work that the surgeon misread her form and confused the requirements. Still, she does alright with comedy roles in TV series.

"Business?" I echoed. "Indeed it's on business. Oh, yes, it's on business all right!" I added, "You bet!" It made the whole thing sound even more busty.

"I see. Well, can I take a message or would you like to come in now and talk to *me* about it?" I couldn't decide whether she sounded menacing or just intrigued. Or even bored. Vets' ladies are often bored and even friendless. Who wants to take tea with a Siamese yowling downstairs. Eclairs have little appeal when there's a diagram of pigs' entrails left with a bottle of something marked 'HORSE' on the low Regency table in front of the sofa.

Inside the house, it was surprisingly quiet. No squeaks or howls. A white Persian cat slid gently over the bannisters and vanished. A couple of white Lhasa Apsos, immaculately groomed, with dark eyes and oriental inscrutability, were curled together on a wicker chair, basking in the sunlight from a glassed-in extension where, once, a kitchen might have been. There was music on a hi-fi. The scent of jasmine. The door to a small office was open and that, too, was tidy, in spite of the usual commercial confetti. There was a desk with neatly clipped paperwork here and there but that was merely impressive. There was, of course, a rolltop in the corner. Any vet worth his Final Demands proves it at once by getting a rolltop and then adding the Ercol. After that, he can sit with his feet up on *The Jersey Herd* volumes 1–5 and read *Penthouse*.

We sat in the sunny extension where there was a tray of coffee, as if she'd been expecting someone. Her cup was full and she poured mine from a graceful grey pot. She said she always put an extra cup ready, but didn't say who she was ready for. She indicated a plate with Mr Kipling Maids of Honour. At least she couldn't cook, I thought, relieved to find a crack in the enamel. I had just broken up the nut milk bar and was offering a piece and trying to encourage a girlish matiness by popping a piece in my mouth at the same time (this would also show I wasn't trying to poison her to get at the drugs cupboard) when she suddenly smiled and relaxed. We could have been chums at once and I could have enrolled her help to get Mr Hebditch on my side, because a vet in the family can be important in any canine institution, but at that moment a small wedge of nut sought out my vulnerable tooth. The one with the hole in it. Closing my jaws was suddenly the most unspeakable agony that brought tears to my eyes. I sat with my mouth hanging open and my eyes watering like a spaniel.

She said, "I'm afraid I don't have very long." I hastily drank some coffee, trying to keep it from running down my chin, while aiming it towards the nut particle for a complete washout. I reckoned I didn't have very long either unless I removed the nut. I wonder if bloodhounds have holes in their teeth? It would explain those pleading eyes and the dribble. I wondered what she had to do so urgently. Maybe she had a pie baking or a mother-in-law in the bath. Vets' ladies don't often have lovers upstairs impatient under duvets, because lovers get turned off by the smell of ether or canker, and it clings to shirts and sheets alike. I heard about one who said he was more in fear of rabies than babies.

"I won't keep you," I assured her, talking funny because my mouth was open to keep the pressure off the nut. "I just wanted to talk about boarding."

"Oh, the timber for the extension?" she said, looking relieved. "You can leave the estimate if you like."

"No, no," I cried, "boarding. I'm starting a Boarding Kennels for holiday dogs just out of town here. A mile off the Motorway. Someone bred 'them messy things' there, the postman says. Your husband would know, I'm sure. I want him to visit me on a regular basis. I hope we can come to some arrangement mutually suitable . . ." I meant cheap rates for a package deal but it sounded better in longer words.

"I'm sure he'd love to," she said with sarcasm.

I went on desperately. "I'm not breeding, not yet. I thought he might help me with that sort of thing during the off season, when I have more time." Now she was laughing at me. It did sound odd, I suppose.

"He'll be very glad you called, and thrilled you need assistance. He's very accomplished at that sort of thing," she said. "He's an engineer, but quite a virile one. I'm the vet."

Her name was Henrietta, but everyone called her Hetty. She had a great sense of humour, too. She accepted a piece of nut milk and lent me a toothpick. She was an Instant Friend, the kind where you add laughter and stir briskly. She was my first friend in the area and for a long time my only one. It was like love at first sight, only a bit more reliable.

Without Hetty, found by accident, I would merely have chalked up another disaster.

4

It was early summer. Like the birds, we usually feathered our nests in spring and, like any hen, I was the one to stay around and mind the eggs. You can't get away from nature in the end. This time, the nest was a rambling old house of brick and slate, with outbuildings, a gazebo in a state of siege with itself, a ha-ha and an overgrown tennis court. The previous owners, incensed by twentieth-century encroachment on their nineteenth-century living standards, had finally admitted defeat and departed to live on an island. The place had stood empty and forgotten for several years before some astute young estate agent discovered it there – a mere footnote on a list of hopeless propositions – and suggested it to us when we asked for anything unwanted by everyone else.

It was the Motorway that killed it for them and the Motorway that made it for me. Round about lay fields of all colours in jigsaw shapes. Hedges had been allowed to stay in that part of the county, and they sprawled in wavery lines and uneven patches of spring shading. First thing in the morning, the world outside the windows seemed to hang from trees, fading in rising mists, spangled muslin over natural scaffolding. It was really too remote for a woman on her own, but a woman whose husband has been snatched into hospital rarely has much choice about her own preferences and when I stood looking down across the wide open country, it was always the Motorway that comforted and enthralled me most.

In the early morning, with a safe night behind me, the richness of steaming coffee round me, morning papers, toast and the radio in front of me, there was no other place I would have chosen to be. "Count your credit," my mother would cry as blessings began to go out of fashion, and credit lay about me like a bulging bank balance.

Of course, on the debit side I had too much to do and no one to listen when I said so.

I suffer from being gregarious the way some people suffer from gumboils. I'm the one who loves to find herself in the middle of a party: the lady who looks forward to walking across a room full of people I never met before, like dipping into a bag of mixed sweets. I enjoy bus queues at rush hours and sale time at Selfridges, the hot excitement of fairgrounds on bank holidays. Why, then, the wide open isolated spaces? Most of us make compromises. This was mine.

I had a husband who yearned to trudge muddy ruts on faraway

farmland. I had a horse I adopted when it was too close to the canning factory for comfort. Neither could be disregarded entirely, if at all. Then there was The Collection – innumerable articles of furniture, objets d'art (known as junk to the uninitiated), Victorian paintings which rambled across even the most enormous walls, brass fenders and even such absurd things as a sedan chair, a fifteen-foot crocodile skin and sundry four-poster beds.

I never could miss an auction or resist a rummage and I was a fall guy for every white elephant for miles around. I collected old books like some people get hooked on alcohol. In the beginning, Victoriana had been the Cinderella of the dealing fairy-tale, but it was as much as I could then afford and as we always had room for my mistakes in the vast mausoleums we found equally unwanted (no one but deluded fools were ready to endure those icy passages and staggering repair bills), my strange tastes and acknowledged blunders stayed with us and finally, to everyone's surprise, became antiques. We trundled them round from house to house, accumulating en route but never distributing, and every time my husband's work demanded a move, somewhere larger and yet larger to house the ever-growing Collection took precedence over anything more practical and less demanding.

I could see the Motorway was going to be my one contact with those hypothetical guests across a crowded room, for ever out of reach. The Motorway, like a rainbow with the crock of gold always out of sight, and those tiny, shiny, coloured toys racing towards it would remind me, yet again, of what I was missing. Now Pa lay fretfully at the end of the same rainbow as well. It was impossible for me to keep the stringent visiting hours and get back here in one day. To be away for even a few hours was going to be out of the question, especially with the bevy of boarders I was hoping to coax. We would both have to accept the inevitable fact of separation for as long as it took.

The sealyham Bustle was restless that first night. She chewed her way steadily through my bedside lampshade in some kind of nervous protest. The lampshade lay in shreds on my pillow when I woke up and I thought the ceiling had come in. Bella had remembered to bring along the felt mouse Bustle took to bed at home, and I woke once or twice during the night under the impression that any disturbance was Bustle gnawing its tail, not my tassels. But by morning, she'd established squatter's rights to a corner of the eiderdown, a bit of purple fringe still clinging to her whiskers, and was sound asleep. She liked a saucer of tea in the morning, too, so I took it up and forgave the indulgence on the grounds it made good publicity for future advertising.

The ad., to appear in our local paper, came out before the wider, networked edition. The days between could be spent in creating a businesslike atmosphere with overtones of homely comfort. I needed an office for a start.

Marsha rang during breakfast. "Darling," she cooed down the phone, "I thought of you such a lot last night."

I was touched. Underneath her apparent self-absorption, Marsha is really rather sweet.

She went on, "It's getting to be so hot in London. I just wondered, darling, how would it be if I brought the Fraction up to you? There's been a weeny bit of aggro with the tenants in the flat below. They say the violins frighten the au pair. No one would hear the boys up with you and we could keep you company for a week or two."

I would hear them. What's more, she would expect me to feed them and admire them and provide them with the basic necessities of life, especially my unwavering attention.

There was no time for excuses. I just said, "Sorry, Marsha. It's *quite* impossible." She said she understood, but *completely*, and I was to have a *super* time and we'd keep in touch. I suppose she thought I had someone with me already. No other reason would have seemed feasible to Marsha, if it wasn't a man.

I returned to the question of an office. These I usually situate between the kitchen range and the fridge, allowing for all variations in taste and weather conditions. I like to spread myself over a wide wooden table, keep my feet on a woolly dog and stretch out for the kettle. I like to be able to relieve boredom with a quick snatch at the cheese, or a few crumbs of corned beef. All any home really needs is a huge kitchen for comfort, a vast hall to repel invaders, and a beautiful romantic bedroom to encourage occupants. I decided to attack those three areas first, and let the rest follow later – if and when I had time for any of it.

Dutifully I rang the hospital night and morning. The patient was always "comfortable" (which was more than I was) and I made sure he understood why it was impossible for me to visit. But though *he* might appreciate it, the staff didn't, and I sensed a growing coldness each time I spoke to one of them. In the old days, it was made difficult for families to visit patients. One hour, twice weekly, was considered ample. A visitor would be sent off on the toe of Sister's boot if appearing at any other time. Now that visiting is often unlimited, visitors are expected to live on the doorstep, whatever difficulties there might be at home, or they're immediately branded as indifferent. My husband wasn't too bothered and that's all that should have mattered, but disapproval turns me blue, and I fretted with undercurrents of guilt. Calls to my husband were guarded: "There's a hole in the roof" is no match for a tranquiliser at bed-time, and his "I think they're keeping something from me" didn't just mean they were refusing to send up a gin with his dinner.

I decided to drive into town after lunch. Bustle was perfectly happy with an afternoon nap. She understood the drill as soon as I handed her the luckless mouse, grabbing it in her teeth and leaping straight on the eiderdown. My own dogs were content to stay and guard the place and settled down at strategic points when I said I was going out, alert to all dangers from alien encounters. I praised their noteworthy attention to duty, whereupon they promptly fell asleep.

This time I put the car in a proper car park where I paid heavily for an old man in a white coat and peaked cap to doze peacefully in a hut out of sight of everything. I had to hope that under these conditions no one would try and flog my car for a fiver before I could collect it again. I think it must have been the picture of Felix on the bonnet they were after. Mickey is anybody's mouse, but Felix walks only for me, painted there by an ex-lover who wanted to be able to spot my car in a hurry.

I had to be able to assure clients that a diet of good, fresh meat would be served daily to all comers – as much as anything because the cost of tins would be monstrous for the numbers I confidently expected by midsummer. A slaughterhouse had been recommended by Humphrey, and rejected by me without hesitation, but I felt there must be at least one butcher in town who could offer me rough beef cheap for large quantities. I carefully overlooked the fact that these days rough beef goes into sausages and pies and ends up as valuable as fillet. The Yellow Pages, my guide and friend, showed five butchers rampant among a sea of supermarkets, and I made a list of their names and addresses.

Mr Moss wore a straw hat and striped apron and had a row of skinned rabbits swaying delicately in the breeze emanating from a faulty fridge motor. He looked the kind of butcher who ran his business like a harem, choosing his favourites by their financial assets. These probably ranged from weekly hand-outs to reciprocation among trades. I waited my turn without much hope, bought some stewing steak, and tried the wistful approach. "I don't suppose you've got anything going spare, have you?" He raised his eyebrows so high his hat fell off the back of his head. I added hastily, "For the dogs, I mean." He went off into the back and I heard it all being repeated and loud guffaws following. I stood my ground. He came back stuffing two lumps of fat pork into a bag, screwed the top into a knot and handed it to me. I thanked him as effusively as I would if he'd presented me with the cheque for a win on the Pools. Then he said "Twenty all right?"

Bewildered, I said, "Pence?" and he snorted "Give it me in notes if you like, lady, and I'll throw in a date at the Mog and Strings!"

It made me doubt the furtherance of our trading relationship. Anyway, how could I explain I would be wanting enough to feed forty for a week? Especially after the magnanimous way he screwed and sealed the bag, a gesture of his generosity. Twenty pence for the contents was nothing short of an outrage. I went on to see who was being kind-hearted in Kindleman's.

There was nobody in Kindleman's at all. No one buying the long, thin, pale strings of home-made sausages, or the scrawny plucked chickens. Mrs Kindleman glowered from the enclosed cash desk, like one of their Christmas turkeys in a cage, purple-wattled and suspicious. Tiles froze the place into immobility.

I'm always intimidated by tiles. I never go near a public loo. I seize up in bathrooms Marleyfied and aseptic and, however tasteful the arrangement of Dutch boys and girls on a splashback, I'm put off by their glaze and lack of warmth. Once, on a diet, I tiled the edge of the kitchen table with mosaic and lost half a stone in ten days. Maybe if we just made use of our antipathies it would be a lot easier to stop smoking, lose weight, reach our potential and marry the right man, but I'm not sure. So often the right man *is* our antipathy at one and the same time and only later turns out to be witty as well.

I bought some kidney to go with the stewing steak and then left. The Kindlemans weren't going to be lavish with their scraps, the anaemic sausages proved that. I did ask outright in Ball and Penry's because the four assistants were in white coats and looked prosperous as well as very jolly. I was using a selection of the right smiles and a thick covering of sticky charm, and the interior of the shop was full of spry bonhomie. It was easy enough to ask about meat for the dogs between merry quips. The young man serving me said, "Certainly. Pet Mince 15p a pound" and swept a lot of churned-up fat into the scales. Before I could find a gag suitable to refuse it, he had the bag of rubbish in my basket wished me good-day and robbed me of 45p. As I backed away, he was swishing his knife round a chunk of beef for a lady in a pixie hood.

The next butcher's was shut. I had begun to realise I was not going to be the most popular lady to hit town that morning. I was almost glad the notice swinging behind the glass said "CLOSED TILL 2". Obviously they were all down the local enjoying a riotous assembly on the strength of their takings in doggies' dinners. I was about to give up and fall back on a crate of Barker's Bonzo when I drew level with the supermarket near the car park.

Just as tiles are anathema, so are supermarkets lady-bait of the worst possible kind. They couldn't be more of a lure if they were crowded with bronzed Tarzans swinging squash rackets and athletic hips. It's not just the streamers laughing off 5p from toothpaste to every buyer of rolled ribs (although there was a nice one which read OUR TEA HAS GONE DOWN THIS WEEK, which did seem a good way for tea to go), it's the general air of eager trading and persuasion that makes me feel they really *want* me to be there. Small shops often have the opposite effect and I feel nothing so much as uneasily aware I'm taking up their time which could be better used totting up the till or talking to friends.

The Butchery had a bell outside which invited anyone to ring for attention. No one enjoys attention more than me, even Fraction in Action. I rang and then stood back waiting for a bronzed genie to appear.

To my amazement one actually did, from the door behind me. He had on a white coat and a woolly cap with a bobble, but he was very attractive, with the skin of a water-weekender, and eyes like those of the cattle he so ruthlessly hewed in private. His smile would have melted dripping.

"Oh, hullo." Smiles Nos. 1, 2, 3 in rapid succession. "Do you sell anything for pets?" "Pieces" sounded excessive; "scraps" gave a nasty impression, like snarls and yelps. Not that any of mine would ever scrap. I have a theory that dogs only fight when they sense your own fear that they will. They know what you have in mind – whether it's going to bed, out for a drink or just round the bend. You watch it next time. It's that sixth sense, and if you think they're going to gang up and spring on next-door's Pom, it's like an order. No one catches on to insecurity more rapidly than Rover.

I drove home with a carton full of unwanted ends, of this and that, bits and tits, and another carton of pigs' heads, looking like a pop group on tour, peering happily out of my open boot. Underneath were an assortment of odd ears and some rather eager trotters. For a fixed and reasonable sum, I managed to corner the supermarket on a weekly supply of domestic rejections. "Nothing condemned," swore Steve, who listened with sympathy to my entire story, practically lifelong, over the frozen breasts. We arranged a weekly call on Wednesday and my thanks obviously embarrassed him. He edged away nervously, his ears reddening. Passing customers must have wondered what on earth was going on between us. But it must have been good for business because at least four paused by the New Zealand legs to listen, and finally felt obliged to buy something when I gave them one of my Sudden Looks, usually reserved for men drivers who cut in on me because they can't bear to see a woman any place but one step behind.

There was a small boy sitting on the fence by the gate when I got home. I said "Hi!" and stopped the car next to him. He wore a pair of well-cut French jeans, no shoes and a tight tee shirt. His hair was shaped, not chopped. Prep. School was written all over him. I'm not arguing whether it's a good thing or nòt. I'm just saying it's a bit more pleasant than blatant Comprehensive, and you can call me Maggie. He slid off the fence and said, "Hullo," and we both smiled. Then he added, "This is Lady."

Lady was a dog of no distinguishable breed, but she had a coat any yak would have saved for Sundays. It was difficult to see which end was which, but when I said "Hi, Lady!", the far one shimmied with such enthusiasm that for a second I caught the flash of brown eyes and blunt nose near me. When the flurry of fur settled and we were back to a carwash mophead, I said "She's terrific!"

I really meant it. Lady was the kind of dog that appears in strip cartoons and calendars, on jigsaw puzzles and boxes of chocolates, accompanied by tatty kids and glossy models. But mainly Lady was a dog who had assimilated a score of virtues from twice as many varieties of ancestors. I often think humans inherit the worst bits of their forebears, but dogs only the best.

I leant out of the car window. "And you?" I asked. The kid said, "I'm Adam Adair," and he held out a small clean hand. We shook, then I held open the passenger door and they got in. The dog stayed on the floor of the car with an instant obedience I found very touching. As we drove up to the house Adam said, agonisingly direct, "Please would you look after Lady when I go back to school?"

A term's twelve weeks. I thought, joyfully, "That's regular money, baby," but then I wondered why the kid had come and not his mother. In business, it's these little points which raise doubts in an astute tycoon.

"Let's talk about it over something to eat," I suggested. With kids you don't offer a drink to show hospitality. Bacon-and-barley flavoured crisps, say, or chocko chips. My own children still fish about in the cupboards when they reappear at home from some distant Hilton, though they all left us to join the Beer or Martini Belt long ago. But maybe they'd dive in the wine cellar if we had one . . .

When we were back in the sun with a couple of jam tarts and some Custard Crunchies between us, I said, "Now – you'd like me to have Lady *all* the time you're at school?"

He nodded. Then he said, reluctantly, "It's Mummy." He paused and I waited. It came out at a rush, all the pent-up anxiety. "She needs brushing a lot, you see, and no one at home has time. She gets terribly knotty and shaggy." He looked up at me, pleading. I had to remind myself he was talking about the dog, not his mother. She sounded a lot less attractive than Lady, anyway. "And she likes pretending to answer the phone, and running three times round the fishpond before supper, and her Mincies. She's scared of thunder and Mr Hollingbury and people sneezing." He stopped and we both stared at Lady with respect. She turned her head modestly aside as if apologising. I'd rarely heard of anyone so discriminating and sensitive.

"Did Mummy say it was OK to bring Lady to me?"

"Well, no, not yet. I thought I'd better see what *you* said before I asked her. But she's always saying Lady's a nuisance, so I think she'd say it was all right."

"I can't be sure about Mr Hollingbury or sneezing," I warned him, "but I'd bear all that in mind, of course, and comfort her in thunder. She could answer the phone any time. I'd be obliged, actually. Running round the fishpond's OK, though it's a bit low on water at the moment, let alone fish, but I think I could manage the rest for her."

"Thanks! Thanks! I think if she's somewhere different she won't need all those things. She might even get to like sneezes and thunder. Not Mr Hollingbury, of course, but I mean it would all be new, wouldn't it? So she wouldn't think of thunder like Mummy being in a temper or the time Mr Hollingbury booted her out, or . . ." He stopped, realising he might be going too far.

"That's true enough," I agreed, "and I can manage Mincies." He looked at me, his eyes fixed on mine, begging me to promise I'd relieve him of all that worry crammed into the small head.

"I'd really love to have her," I assured him warmly, quelling the tycoon trying to get out, "and I promise I'll keep her well, brushed and always happy. But we must get your parents' permission first, of course."

"They won't care." He shook his head. "Mummy doesn't like her and Daddy lives in France."

I wondered how anyone could dislike Lady. She sat near the Custard Crunchies and didn't even lick her lips. I gave her half my jam tart and she spilt not a crumb. I said gently, "You see, it could be rather expensive." I had to say it. There had to be a way out for Mummy, anyhow.

"That's OK," Adam said eagerly. "I get 50p a week pocket money in term and you can have it all. I saved £2 from my holiday money and you can have that, too." I pushed his hand back in his pocket.

"Look," I said, wondering how I could explain 50p was a mere drop in the dog bowl, "let's talk to Mummy first. Give me your phone number and I'll ring her. If Lady hears the phone tomorrow morning, I shan't mind a bit if she answers it."

I meant it as a mild joke but it was too big a problem for laughing.

"I do try and stop her, honestly. Mummy gets so cross. She once threw a riding-boot and it hit Lady over the eye." And she could take it, I thought, with all that shaggy armoury, but I could see it had hurt the boy much more.

We sat and talked about school and Lady and his holidays and her toe-nails, which grew rather curly and needed watching. I thought he said "washing" and in all seriousness I suggested a nail-brush, used regularly. Adam said, "Watching, not washing," and a slow smile, his first since he arrived, spread all over his face. After that we grew less serious and often laughed.

Mummy appeared to be away a lot. Daddy rarely appeared from France. Adam didn't mind because it was easier when he was at home to be with Grannie and Mrs Hollingbury. Grannie stayed in her room most of the time and though Mrs Hollingbury refused to have Lady in the kitchen, dining-room or sitting-room and certainly not upstairs, Adam somehow managed to smuggle her round the house one jump ahead of detection. He said he was getting jolly good at talking to the empty lean-to shed where Lady was supposed to sleep, when really she was up in his bedroom snoozing in the sunshine. They went out together a lot. He said Lady understood just about everything. I didn't doubt that at all.

I told him I had to unload some pigs' heads from the car and I wasn't looking forward to it. Adam said he'd like to help. He said you couldn't possibly think of them as being anything to do with real cosy old pigs, could you? It was, he said, like dead people – like his grandfather. He had been told his grandfather was dead when Grannie came to live with them, and yet the grandfather he knew played Monopoly and mended the electric race-track and then broke it again, showing everyone how well he'd done it. People were alive things, weren't they? So were pigs.

We loaded up the barrow with the week's supply. When I counted, I found there were ten heads and innumerable spare parts. I wondered what on earth I was going to do if I didn't get enough customers to enjoy the pork dinners I'd be cooking from now on. God, I thought, cooking! How do you cook a pig's head except as a roast with an orange in its mouth, and a frill at its neck? I was sobered to such an extent I went very quiet. I kept thinking, "You and I, Adam, we both have problems." But Adam was saying thank you and suggesting midday as the best time to speak to Mummy. And then he went.

I added a mug of coffee to the remaining jam tarts, and called it lunch. Then I drove down to the village shop. Tomorrow the advertisement would appear and I'd be inundated with calls, crowded with holiday dogs bent on having a good time, and tied to the house for the rest of the summer. Today was for organisation and local support.

The village was four miles away. It had no thatched cottages nor village green. Just a row of small houses, some old, some new, on either side of the narrow road. It began with a garage and pumps, ended with the primary school and scout hut. The church stood aloof half way down on a slight incline with a bare graveyard behind it. Six council cottages had that inevitable stamp of charity so much more attractive in old almshouses. The group had been awarded chain link fencing, with its harsh reminder of authority and restricted freedom.

The village shop was next to the schoolhouse and had a swinging sign which said "WALLS". Someone from the pub opposite, after closing perhaps, had painted a large "B" over the "W" in red enamel. There was a pillarbox let into the wall and a phone box near the bus stop. Buses ran two days a week and at weekends in summer. It was, in fact, a pretty average English village, unpretentious, sober and static.

Over the shop door the name of Misses Priddle was confined to small print. The only sign of tradition were the two bow windows, newly put in, and the pink undercoat on one was reminiscent of respectable underwear. Village shops rarely have names, though I once saw one called Nancy's Pantry. The young couple who took it over decided it might be misconstrued and told the village that they felt sure it would be understood if they changed it. They rather liked the Pantry bit, so just changed the first word to the wife's name which, unfortunately, was Pansy.

I went in hesitantly. There were two ladies behind the counter and three in front of it. One was waiting to be served, another was piling up bread, tins and biscuits in a wire basket, and a child was turning over the Chews and Licks department. A third woman was paying her bill and about to leave. When she saw me she stopped and began to browse through a pile of new magazines, ears akimbo. I took a wire basket and began edging round the shelves. It dawned on me how much wire signifies our current way of life – fences, baskets and barbed. All severely practical, utilitarian and harsh.

I knew I was forcing a strange self-consciousness on them all. I was an unwelcome audience to a very private scene. I might have walked in on an orgy. So when it came to my turn, the child served, the women ready to leave, in an uneasy and subdued atmosphere, I introduced myself. The lady at the magazines who looked like an enquiring tortoise, moved on to the birthday cards.

"I'm opening a Boarding Kennels at The Hollies," I said, back on old Smile 6 and pushing over my basket loaded with goodies, "so if you hear of anyone wanting to board a dog, do let me know, won't you? I'll leave you my number to pass on and as soon as I've had the printing done, I'll leave some cards as well." One Miss Priddle ran the bacon slicer very very slowly as she watched me. The other began totting up from my shopping. I went on, "Now, groceries. Do you deliver?"

I felt sure they didn't, but I had to show this could be a mutually beneficial relationship. I thought it would end in my favour only when they had to admit they fell down on the delivery end, then I could leave my cards there with a clear conscience as I headed back to the supermarket and reduced prices.

But the taller, greyer-haired Miss Priddle, pausing mid-cash-up, said quickly, "Yes, of course we do. Tuesday your way," and went on checking the toilet rolls and cornflour in my wire basket.

I was taken aback. I said "Gosh" and "Super" like a fourth-former given a new hockey-stick. Then I suddenly realised I was speaking the truth before it had actually dawned on me, because even at village shop prices it *would* be easier and cheaper than going into town. Even if I could leave the dogs, which I couldn't, town luxuries were not for me, and it might be better to keep out of temptation. At 50p a day for big dogs and 30p for smaller ones, I was hardly going to corner the market as a crazy capitalist. I could reckon on just about two tee shirts per annum plus wellies for winter, but anything more reckless would have to wait until all the outstanding bills were paid and someone else was taking back his major responsibilities. Anyway, I had already decided to lay up the car for the rest of the summer to save expense.

The smaller Miss Priddle had a golden rinse over the grey and several teeth to match both. They spoke without any dialect and that made me nervous. I like ladies in village shops to call me "m'dear" or "luv" and bob about in front of huge glass sweet jars.

"Fabulous," I added. And then, "Fantastic." You'd have thought they were offering me their entire stock for free. They glanced at me curiously as I babbled on, "Such a lovely little place." (It was chromed, glassy and horrible.) "Bet it's a little goldmine." Words escaped, rolled on downhill, gathering speed. I forgot people get insulted if you compliment success that's merely financial.

"We may have to give up," declared the golden Priddle, like a Rhode Island Red bustling round a clutch of eggs. "We can't make ends meet in competition with your Straightways and your Feel Frees." I'd never heard such splendid variations on supermarket names and I gazed at her in admiration. But she didn't laugh. Her beak was shut tight. So I said, "Oh dear! Not yet I hope?"

"We're seeing what the summer brings," she said darkly. Her sister added, "But we hope to open a Rest Home in Newhaven if we can buy something suitable. For the Closing Years." I wondered if she meant theirs or their patients. "Should you hear of anyone or anything. . . ?" It was like exchanging magazines when you've read them. *Penthouse* for *Needlewoman*. Tit for Tat.

I went home feeling I had at least laid some foundation for my own enterprise, anyway. Two customers already, if you could count Lady: the ad. out next day, feeding all organised and groceries to be delivered. Surely I couldn't fail now. The sunshine made me heady with hope.

But when the sun went down in the evening, I suddenly felt the ground shift under my feet and confidence drain away. The house was screechingly empty of human voices. Outside the night pressed against the huge windows making me feel surrounded by hostility. Desperately I needed comfort. Almost in tears I rang the hospital.

The Sister on Frimley Ward was as acid as ever. She knew I was on long distance rates and said "One moment, please," while she kept me hanging on as a punishment. She tidied her desk and filed a few nails. Then she came back to the phone and said impatiently "Yes?" I said "Good evening, Sister. How are you?" and she said, "Speak up, please," as if I wasn't really trying. Then she told me to hold on, as if to a patient un-cooperatively dying at the end of her duty rosta.

She never would say how she was and always avoided any direct answers to anything. After a good six minutes listening to the clicks which ticked away money, I put my mouth right up to the phone and shrieked "*Help!!!!!!*"

"Why?" my husband said in a puzzled voice, adding, "I was just enjoying the play on BBC2." He sounded hurt. I felt sure his eardrum was.

I said, "Oh, I *am* sorry," meaning about the yell and he said he guessed if we were quick he wouldn't miss the nude scene the papers warned would shock those of a delicate disposition. The whole of Men's Medical and Surgical had been sitting patiently waiting since *Crossroads*, even the critical cases. It gave the nurses a rest from bedpans, backrubs and blanket baths.

"No, I mean sorry I yelled, only I've been hanging on for ages."

"That's OK," Pa assured me. "There's this bit about this bird who had this thing about this bloke and I . . ."

"How are you?" I asked unnecessarily.

"OK, why?" He sounded as annoyed as Sister at being asked. Really, I thought, you might imagine people were in hospital for anything but their health. What goes on to get everyone touchy about the sort of polite enquiry you make all the time in the Public Library?

"You'd know soon enough if I wasn't," he grumbled. "They keep on at me to know why you're not coming to find out." This after he'd repeated time and again that he would much rather I stayed near his silver christening spoon.

"I do have a bit of self-preservation to consider," I protested loftily. "Just remind them I stage-managed an entire removal single-handed, and then set up a business to keep us both from starving in our declining years." He grunted. It was hardly the tender exchange I planned and so desperately needed. I wondered why we always seemed like wary strangers on the phone.

"OK, OK," he muttered. "This call's costing about two years of anybody's business. You'll hear when there's something to know about. I wouldn't ring here too often, though. They don't like it." Emotion, I told myself takes a funny way out for most men. Probably he was fighting back tears: the lump in the throat, the ache in the heart. Strong pathos under that lovable gruff exterior.

But he ruined that line of charitable thinking. His voice warmed, and it wasn't for me. "The blonde bit's seducing the feller with the sideburns," he added excitedly. "I can spot them through the glass door. Must go and see what happens next."

I hoped he meant the play because if this was what went on in Frimley Ward no wonder they all got so tetchy over enquiries about their wellbeing.

I put down the phone and wandered back into the kitchen. The dogs had all gone to their respective beds, except for Bustle who was waiting upstairs to spring under the eiderdown when I took off the bedspread. I thought how glad I'd be when the house was full of barks and paws and shaggy ears: and loving brown eyes that stayed loving. Dogs, I thought bitterly, have a greater capacity for true love than any man. And a real sense of priorities and values.

In the vast silence of my own company I went slowly to bed, remembering there was no chance of a bath until I could light the boiler, and the boiler could hardly be lit until there was something to put on it, and there wouldn't be much to put on it until I could order fuel.

I stood in the dark and watched slats of light from the Motorway streaming past, a long way off, to get even further down the bend of the rainbow, and I wished I were one of them. A plane, moving across the black sky and tracked by its wing lights, came suddenly from nowhere and disappeared, just as suddenly, into eternity. Like a shooting star, I thought, one glorious moment for everything. Maybe I, too, would have mine eventually. Not here, though: not with spaniels and poodles and pekes and pigs' heads.

I gave a great sob of self-pity and put my head under the blanket as if I could get away from reality. The next moment something heavy settled on my neck. I emerged a few inches – and a tongue met my ear. I wasn't alone, nor forgotten, nor unloved and unneeded. Someone cared, even if it was only Bustle. I put out a hand and fondled her ears, and she crept closer, sighed and snuggled in to sleep. She was still close to me when I woke and found the world calling to me in bird song outside the window.

5

The local weekly newspaper came out the same day and the phone began to ring before nine o'clock. Yes, Mrs – er – Wallis, was it? You're very lucky. A sudden cancellation leaves a vacancy for your little Muffin. A case of shingles in the family. No, not mine. The client's: having to cancel their holiday. Two weeks from Friday? Fine. I see, Mrs Wallis. Yes, well, of course. Naturally. If Muffin is going to get hysterical on his own in an outside chalet (chalet? who did she think we were? the Pom Pontin's?) I will have him with me indoors. My bedroom? He doesn't like to be alone? Certainly, Mrs Wallis. Does he need a nightlight, too? No, Mrs Wallis, only joking, of course. My bed? Well, it's fairly busy just now. I mean, there's quite a few of us in it. Quite a bit of activity, if Muffin doesn't mind. Like the traffic at Hyde Park Corner! But he's welcome to join us. Not a lot of lampshade left for snacks, though.

I graciously waived the flood of gratitude – which included a cure for shingles to be passed on where needed. In the course of time, I was given tips and hints and recipes and advice from so many clients, I would have worked out cheaper than *Chambers Encyclopaedia*.

The paper had arrived with the morning post. I turned at once to the column marked PETS. Nothing. Well, "Cuddly Pugs for £20" or "Why not have a Peke for £50?" There was also someone prepared to strip for a nominal fee according to size. Huh, I thought, I bet she's doing all right on the phone this morning. Why hadn't I chosen a sexy line like that? Where, in point of fact, *was* my ad. anyway?

The toast popped and I buttered a slice and poured the tea from a coffee-pot. The sun shone encouragingly through the window. Mattie and Rosie sat bolt upright on either side of my chair hoping for crusts. Rosie would bury hers under my wellies. She was a prudent dog with an eye to a lean tomorrow. They didn't share my passion for toast, but they appreciated the gesture that offered it. The radio played "Guatanamara" which is far and away my favourite sound. Nothing, not even the newspaper's missing words which were to have made my fortune, could daunt the high spirits which rose with me and the birds on a sunny morning.

And then I saw it, in the first column, framed, under PERSONAL. I never did find out why it was there, but so successful did it become that I placed a repeat in the same place all summer. It read "HOW

ABOUT OLD WRECKS THEN?" I had to read it several times before its odd familiarity struck home. Fusty's Mum must have dictated it over the phone, but it certainly was eye-catching . . . Old Rex would never have had the same appeal. I mean, everyone's got an old wreck somewhere, in the garage or attic, the spare room or the Sunset Home, or even waiting for retirement in an office down-town.

By lunchtime the phone had rung fifteen times and I was promising shelter, love and innumerable little personal services of an individual nature "He likes to play pat-a-cake at bedtime" ". . . must have his tea in a cup, but he'll bring his own" "She has her own little chest, labelled, of course, if you'll just help her take the right pills when it's time" – and, too, ". . . a good six miles a day and no heel-taps!" (What *could* that mean?) I made notes all over the wall by the phone, on my shirt sleeve, the phone book and the back of the Rates Demand. I even filled the STOP PRESS space in two old newspapers lining a drawer and the page for 25th December in my diary. I would have to turn it all into proper records, a lined exercise book or something. I'd have to run proper accounts and keep a desk diary.

I really dreaded all that part. I meant to avoid capital outlay as far as I could. Why earn a fiver to spend a fiver in getting it?

I turned out a few more tea chests and found a hard-backed exercise book with lined pages and a margin, a cash column and the word "Parsley" underlined at the top left hand corner. After that it read "4 boxes" and there were signs that I'd tried to rub it out again. Not surprising really. I vaguely remembered a failed parsley crop. No one else would have failed with parsley. No one else *could* have failed with parsley. It grows like a weed everywhere except where I'd sown it with care and compost.

The errors of the past, like morning mist, dissolved into the success of the present, however transitory. I tore out the page and printed another bold heading: NAME. That would be column 1. Then I stopped. Did I mean name of dog or owner? I was unsure, so I put next to it OWNER and then ADDRESS and then BREED ARRIVAL FEES DEP . . . and ran off the edge of the page. And tore it out.

And began again. Then I found I'd put BREAD. So tore that out. And then I decided to keep all my notes in a giant paperclip I had somewhere to hold my discarded hairpiece together. Later I would get a proper book and enter it all up. I unpacked another tea chest with Treacle and Frilly the cat, diving in and out of the discarded paper, teasing the tissue and one another. Frilly had this fantastic purr. A pleasure machine without a thermostat. She seemed to gear herself up first thing and only took occasional time off to charge up her batteries with a plate of Feline Fancies.

I was listing my jobs for the day, as a way to avoid actually doing them, when Mr Mathews arrived. A warning came from the dogs in the kitchen, who were idling the time away with an empty shoebox and now began competing for the prize as loudest threat to intruders. I rushed out, falling over what looked like the jawbone of a whale from the pigs' head collection, and some string which wound its weary way from table and chair legs and sagging over to the dresser.

Outside the back door, when I opened it, stood a man.

"My name's Walter Mathews. I rang earlier. This is Teddy."

I said, "Do come in," and patted Teddy gratefully. He was to be my milk and honey; my detergent powder, nail varnish and rate-solvent.

Mr Mathews was middle-aged and his suit had spots on the pockets. It didn't take a psychiatrist or Kojak to tell me he was hard up, family-badgered and tired out. I said, "Hi, Teddy-bear! He's lovely. How long can he stay?" It sounded nicer than, "How much is he going to be worth to me?" And he really was lovely. A cross-bred, humble, middle-class dog. Not one of your out-and-out aristocrats, nor yet a dauntless mongrel. A cross between a bedlington and a bulldog, perhaps, with variations. The wool and the legs. A nice blend of the timid and determined.

"We're off to Clacton," his master said with pride. He bent and fondled the dog's ear. They exchanged glances of trust and love . . . and despair. If Mr Mathews ever gave Mrs Mathews that sort of look, she was a lucky lady. "Back two weeks from tomorrow," he went on bravely. "The kids are crying at home because I've had to bring him over. Can we ring and see he's OK later in the week?"

"Of course you can, any time, often as you like." The ones who keep in touch are the ones who pay the bill without arguing. I took the lead and stepped back inside. Once I started asking in, and offering hospitality, down went the profits. I was going to be tough this time. I had to be. But Mr Mathews hovered.

Then, awkwardly, he said, "There's just one or two things I promised I'd tell you. I mean, he's not a fussy eater. Can't afford to be. Likes a run any time, and always comes when he's called. I have his basket and the bit of an old handbag he likes." He hesitated, then laughed uncomfortably. I waited. He went on at a rush, "Look, it sounds daft, I know, but, well . . . he likes to say his prayers." He stopped again. "You know how it is, the wife's keen on the kids having a balanced view of life, not letting them slide into these permissive ways you read about. She reckons prayer and all that a jolly good thing, even if they don't realise it." He flushed, embarrassed. People talk about their sexual hang-ups with eager conceit, but their religious beliefs have to be turned into practical application.

He went on, "If you'd just see he kneels by his box and folds paws before bed?" I nodded, reassuringly, as if I were prepared for an entire religious revival.

'You don't have to worry, Mr Mathews, honestly," I assured him heartily. "It might even be a good idea to bring the others in and hold a short service."

His diffidence turned to real pain and I was immediately sorry I'd said it. "The kids wouldn't pray if Teddy didn't, you see," he muttered, "and I don't want him to forget – it's not that we think its beneficial for Teddy!"

"And why not?" I cried, rushing into the breach as usual so that I trod on his toes and fell flat on my face at the same time. "He's such a lovely, happy, placid dog. How do we know it isn't through the power of prayer?"

I'd gone too far. Mr Mathews just nodded and turned to go. I added quickly, "Sorry. But I think I do half mean it. And anyway, it's a really charming idea. Oh, look, do come in and have a drink with me! I'm sick of coffee and I'm sick of my own company." Suddenly I knew it was true. I wasn't flattering him or trying to compensate. He turned, sympathy reversed, and I poured us each a small Scotch from a stock of bottles, half empty, left from Christmas.

Mr Mathews sat back on a wooden kitchen chair and began to talk. His hair was thinning and his lean face looked hungry as well as tired. He told me about his family. Four kids, a rented bungalow outside Clacton every year for two weeks, an overworked wife with asthma. Teddy sat on the floor at his feet, eyes appealingly raised, pleading not to be abandoned. They were so very close, the man and the dog, and Mr Mathews hand gently scratched the dog's neck under the collar, and he occasionally smiled down reassuringly. The bond between them was almost unbearably moving.

I felt a lump in my throat that no devotion between father and son could have raised. If his children hated leaving Teddy behind, their father was hating it even more. When he finally rose and handed me the lead, neither of us knew what to say and, in the end, after murmuring something, he turned and fled. Teddy made no effort to follow. He understood completely. He just stood there, very still, staring at the closed door. I knelt down and put my arms round him.

"Come on, Teddy bear," I whispered, letting my tears fall on his nose and wondering who they were really for. "Let's have a bit of something sweet, a kiss and a crisp." OK, so it was bad for his teeth, but losing a tooth can never be anywhere as wretched as losing a loved one into the unknown, and for Teddy that was just what had happened. One of the conditions on which holiday chalets were now let was that no pets could be permitted. It seemed absurd when a dog is usually far less destructive than a child, and more part of a family than Auntie.

And so we all shared some ginger snaps and I introduced Teddy to the rest. Treacle, a short-legged mongrel I'd found years before, lying scared and sore in a ditch, flung from a passing car by someone who regarded life – provided it was not their own – expendable enough to toss into eternity. Rosie I'd picked up in a market, trying to scratch a sore body, flea-ridden and miserable, while shut in a converted grocery carton. And Mattie, an Old English sheepdog who always meant well but managed, unfailingly, to upset everybody. She was grumbling now, under the table, complaining bitterly and resenting the fact that no one was listening. Mattie had been the victim of uncaring owners who absconded from their business and left her locked in a cellar, where she was only found a long time later, starving and thirsty and only just alive.

Treacle was the one who welcomed the newcomers. She had a highly developed social sense, often stepping aside at the water bowl for others to go first, and even inviting a share of her evening Bonio. Teddy waited warily, but Treacle wagged her long feathery tail and widened her grin. Then she slid back on her haunches, Mattie stopped grumbling and Rosie unearthed a bit of biscuit from my wellies and all was well. I went over to the kettle and plugged it in again.

I chattered away to Teddy in the most comforting voice I could find, but his eyes kept turning back to the door; I wondered if I was ever going to get used to these awful emotional moments. I wondered how much suffering you can take for others. I wished I were back with the Parsley.

Then the door-bell rang again. Mrs Wallis and her Muffin were not due till Friday. Could this be Monty, with Mr Friar? I went to the door and it was neither. A girl stood there. She was about fourteen and she wore a mixture of school uniform and bricklayer's assistant gear. Jeans, hobbly surgical-type boots, and a blazer. She was leading a white poodle which stood nervously on its toes. It had a rhinestone collar and blue plaited lead. A dog that would present strong competition for Bustle as Queen of the Day I thought. The girl had a basket with a neat collection of odds and ends inside.

"Willy," she said, handing over the dog. Anyone can make a mistake about sex.

I was tempted to say, "I'm sure he will, given a chance" but she was turning to go, so I grabbed her and said, "Hang about! Who are you? and where does Willy come from? I can't recall a booking for him. Look, you'd better come in and tell me his secrets."

Her name was Marilyn and she brought Willy over for her sister who was getting married the next day. She said there was an awful row going on at home about which family would have the dog. Her sister's mother-in-law-to-be said her son had bought the dog in the first place, even if he had given it to Sarah, so naturally they would have it till the honeymoon was over. Sarah's mother, though she already had a dog, claimed to have been chief sitter-in for the past two years and so of course she would have him. Sarah was sobbing. Doors were slamming.

Marilyn said, "Nobody asked Willy."

In the end they settled the whole thing when Miss Priddle told them about me. Marilyn hoped they might solve it by calling off the wedding. She didn't want to be a bridesmaid and wear pink frills.

Treacle was grinning, showing a row of neatly immaculate teeth, like some miniature Jaws on its best behaviour. Rosie wandered over and stood staring in awe of the vision in white fluff. I said, "Rosie likes him. Funny, because she's usually chummier with bitches."

"That's what Willy is," said Marilyn. "Her name's Wilhelmina Stitch." Well, they all wear coats like that these days, not to mention rhinestones. Even dogs go unisex, or perhaps they started it all.

". . . and she sleeps in Sarah's room," she went on. I might have guessed. "And she likes to catch chocky drops (there's a tin in the basket) thrown from the bed when you get in." I made laborious notes in my exercise book – 'Throw c.drops from bed' under Teddy's praying notes 'paws folded!' I could see I should be fairly occupied at bedtime from now on, throwing and praying and, of course, cuddling Bustle in lieu of anyone else.

"Oh, yes," added Marilyn, "three meals – but all that's there, on the envelope with the pills inside. One a day for her neuroses. I'm going to Paris," she boasted, "on an exchange visit. They're only going to Jersey." She changed to contempt. I said, "Jersey's lovely," though I'd never been there. Sometimes anywhere looks lovely except the sink. She wrinkled her nose. "If I couldn't go somewhere romantic after all that trouble, I wouldn't bother in the first place."

The phone was ringing again so I didn't stop to point out that marriage is about fifty years more than a honeymoon, because sometimes I wondered if it actually was.

Holding the phone in my hand and Willy under my arm, I watched her go.

"If I come round right away," said a sepulchral voice, "will you be able to accommodate *me*?" The words were full of meaning. I said firmly, "If you come round right away or any other time, I'll set my four alsatian killer-dogs on you, and if you ring again I'll send out the sniffers."

He cut off quicker than I did but I suppose I might have expected the weirdos to be at it.

Funny, I thought, I don't get nervous on my own. Not about that kind of thing. Not really. Only of darkness and very still nights: cobwebs and my own inadequacy.

Surely I was safe enough with all these dogs around? Teddy seemed a born protector and Mattie hated most people and all men, though nothing would make her attack unless provoked or requested. The Rescue Society had been afraid of her going to a home where there were children or sheep or men, in that order, but since she'd been with us she'd been the soul of sanctity in the house and a simmering virago outside. Her method with intruders was to knock them down by brute force and then bite. Not Queensberry Rules exactly but I never pointed that out. A word from me and I kidded myself she would let go. I never had to try it out, and I wouldn't be uttering a word, whatever it was, for the salvation of phone funks.

I was about to cook sausages all round, when the phone rang again; I picked up my pen and began looking efficient, but it was Marsha.

"Sweetie," she murmured, "just a warning. A Sheikh Abu Alimar – though he calls himself Mr Follicle, for obvious reasons" (?) "will be ringing you. He wants you to look after his *fleet* – would you believe? – of salukis. Persian gazelle hounds, you know. He has to go back to, well, where he came from (New York, I think) and can't rely on their well-being at his country place in Berkshire. I said you'd be delighted."

"What's a fleet of dogs?" I asked, wondering if it would be five or fifty and just how big a bedroom dog-boarders need. Maybe it would be best to move out into the barn right away. Let the dogs take over the house.

"Oh, well, darling, rather a lot," said Marsha vaguely, "but he's loaded, of course. Loaded. So quote whatever you like. Not that he'll ask. He leaves all that to his accountant. I wondered whether you'd like me and Mischa to pop up for a few days. To help, you see?"

Marsha and Mischa (I think he was plain Mike until Marsha turned him into a fantasy for herself) ran an on-and-off relationship. I was surprised to hear his name. Only a few weeks ago I swear she had told me he killed himself using a jewelled scimitar after a violent quarrel with her.

"I'd love that, Marsha, but not when I can't offer you a bath or heating of any kind. It's all very primitive here . . ."

She sighed. "It's *just* what we long for – dew to wash the feet and rain to rinse the hair." I remembered her twice-weekly visits to Sassoons in Sloane Street and played along.

"Oh, yes, it is," I lied, "especially the straw bedding under the stars and food gathered from hedgerows. Or pigs' heads," I added callously.

I think that was the crunch.

Later I wondered if the freak who'd made the suggestive call was merely the sheikh with his halting English. If so, thank God I'd snapped him off so quickly. I fancied a fleet of salukis as little as I did a phone funk.

I shared the sausages round, chopping them and adding dog meal and the contents of four tins. Teddy, I noticed, carefully ate everything except the biggest bit of sausage which he carried away to bury under the mat, probably with his master in mind. Unfortunately, he chose a bad bit of flooring where very old lino had come away leaving grime and silverfish in equal quantities. And Rosie, always hungry, was watching from the corner of her eye. Poor Teddy, he was probably used to meals with the family and Grace said before and after. It was difficult to get the bit of sausage tucked out of sight, but he managed in the end and then sat close to guard it. Maybe it was his prudent hedge against inflation or something.

Frilly used her sausage slice for mouse practice, throwing and catching and patting it up and down the table before sitting back and nibbling it. I handed round cheese and poured several bowls of milk. From tomorrow, I promised aloud, we'd all be on roast pork at regular intervals. Well, all except me, that is. After cutting up a roast pig's head I knew I'd never look at a bacon buttie again.

The dogs didn't complain: they filled up on ginger snaps and were more than content. Most of them enjoy an occasional change of diet plus something extra tasty as a treat, like ice cream for kids. Any indulgence is seen as a sign of love, and vets who recommend no bits between meals or sweet things from time to time, fail to understand these are like sudden cuddles between lovers, à propos of nothing but deep emotion. We all need the ginger crumbs of occasional reassurance. It's a lot like exercise: no dog *has* to be walked into a heart attack to work its muscles enough. One owner I know killed off three spaniels before they were eight years old. "And it's not as if they didn't get plenty of exercise," she wailed. "I gave every one of them a good five mile run daily, me on my bike and them running beside it. And another good, sharp walk before bed."

Dogs usually know best what exercise they need, according to their age and condition, by the simple method of being active until they're tired. Only the very large ones – and sometimes not even those – should really be taken far. A garden to romp in, even a house with stairs, supplies enough opportunity to take what they want. They love walks to break the monotony or as a chance to be with you. Nobody ever expects us to take a five-mile walk every day on top of our normal exercise, getting to and from work or the shops, round the house or offices and so on; and compare the size we are with the average dog!

One of the most shattering stories I hate to remember was told me by an old man who had lost an alsatian he loved. He was quite convinced it died of a broken heart, and so was I. The vet, on a visit to trim the dog's claws, remarked on its obvious overweight. He said they must cut down on food: no titbits, nothing sweet, no sharing his master's morning toast or bedtime biscuit. The old man told me the dog used to sit there and stare at him, utterly bewildered at being suddenly deprived. At first he thought it was some kind of punishment and slunk about looking ashamed and penitent, then, gradually, it must have dawned on him that love had been withdrawn. He grew thinner and thinner (which would have at least satisfied the vet) and after a few weeks the old man came down one morning and found the dog dead.

The vet was puzzled. Nothing wrong physically, he said. The dog was, in fact, healthier since he'd lost weight. Or he should have been. But the old man knew his beloved pet had died of a broken heart. He told me he saw it in the tragic eyes, the drooping tail, the laid back ears.

Let us remember that a chocky drop thrown from the bed, is not just a chocky drop thrown from the bed. No, indeed. It's a message between two minds, a giving and a receiving of love.

The old man died six months after the dog. Whatever the cause for that, I know in my heart it was hastened by remorse.

With sausages, biscuits and dishes of weak tea all round, I hoped they were comforted by sharing. We all sat together in the tatty old kitchen, the walls waiting patiently, as they had for so long, to be painted and adorned, the original range black and shiny and a wood fire glowing through the bars. The copper pans, pitted and worn from years of use, hung above and reflected flames of gold. OK, so the floor needed re-covering and the pot sink was the size of many a modern bath with just the same cleaning problems, but there was a sense of comfort and peace which cats and dogs, fed and sleeping, loved and needed, shame the restlessness of man and his contemptible dissatisfaction. The urge to change and renovate is alien to animals, who are always perfectly content in just being. Maybe Humanity lost its chance of that when it rejoiced at the opportunity to barter it's woad for a wheel.

I decided on a complete spring-clean before the boarders began to arrive in droves, and let the redecorating wait. And quite early again, I went to bed. My own dogs stayed with Frilly in the kitchen, going to their respective boxes and baskets as I said goodnight. The rest trolled after me upstairs. Bustle took over her reserved spot with a sharp little snap at Willy when she wandered round that side of the bed to have a look. I put Willy's basket close to my bed so I could reach out to reassure her during the night, and she climbed in and sat waiting expectantly for her reward. Teddy stood anxiously concerned about what he should do in these new and difficult circumstances, when God was probably getting impatient.

Feeling a right banana, I folded his paws for him and he sighed with relief as he rested his head against the bedside and closed his eyes. I wasn't sure how it should go, but I said, "Prayers, Teddy," and heard him sigh again gently. Feeling utterly ridiculous, I muttered,

> "Gentle Jesus, even God,
> Look upon this little dog.
> Suffer his simplicities
> Keep him safe from lice and fleas."

It may not have been what he was used to, but it satisfied Teddy and, I hope, God, too. Willy was obviously impressed and she watched Teddy curl up on his blanket in the box which I put at the bottom of my cupboard out of draughts. I hastily threw Willy's chocky drops and gave Bustle a quick cuddle. Then I put out the light.

Just before I fell asleep I remember thinking there may not have been an easier or more delightful way of earning a living, but there surely had to be a less dotty one.

6

I woke up because the phone was ringing. Bustle had a paw in my ear, as though she was trying to stop me hearing it. I like a dog with spirit and determination, even if it be mildly evil, so I kissed her, grabbed something to cover the fact that I sleep in the nude, and ran downstairs.

Once, long ago, the old place had been a school – a small, select, boarding-school for girls – with innumerable plugs for telephones so that bells still rang all over the place. Clutching a half-embroidered altar-cloth I had found in the back of what had once been a needlework cupboard, I rushed from hall to kitchen to study to sitting-room until I remembered the little lobby behind the conservatory. It was there, screaming for attention behind a potted, but dead, azalea.

"Sorry to disturb you," said a man's voice with a trace of humour, "but I've a plane to catch. Can you possibly have my two afghans for a few weeks?"

I had decided to chalk on the kitchen wall "NEVER SAY NO". I already had "LEARN TO SAY NO" which always travels with us from house to house to remind me about over-eating. But I would just have to learn to discriminate between them. I also had "WHEN THE CREDIT'S LOW, ORDER CHAMPAGNE" (to show Fate the defiance she deserved) and across the cooker "NOTHING MATTERS VERY MUCH & MOST THINGS DON'T MATTER AT ALL" which is a help when I burn the potatoes. I love words. Everything I have is decorated by comment, advice, comfort or encouragement, even my knickers. It does help to get one through the days without stress. I use chalk on smooth brown paper which I pin up on white walls, and I planned to make them a more permanent feature of redecoration, when any redecoration happened. I would, I decided, print my sources of inspiration on the walls themselves, each one surrounded by a painted frame. They would be my contemporary version of the old Victorian texts which already lined the walls of my bedroom. I quite looked forward to the result. It's a thing one can do when a man is out of the way. He'd never go along with it otherwise. The idea would shock him, like streaking one's hair green because they don't do it next door, but the end product often passes without being noticed. I always think walls are just waiting to be made interesting and if you can't get Gauguin's Tahiti, get going on graffiti. Life should be all exotic extremes, but men have yet to reach that level of intelligence.

"One moment," I said busily, "I think we can." I pretended to consult my records, fluttering the pages of the phone book close to the earpiece. "Ah, yes. I can *just* get them in. A cancellation. Owners sick of, er, chicken-pox."

"I bet they are," he said with feeling.

"Yes, well, when will you be bringing them?" I glanced round. Afghans aren't like pomeranians. They need folding and storing in the right places. It was barely seven o'clock. Outside I could hear one of those noxious birds who go rattling round like Hearty Harry on a TV Spectacular. I stopped being quite so brisk myself and added, "I don't open till nine a.m."

"Well, actually, I *was* thinking about now?" He had a faint American accent and made the suggestion like a question as Americans often do. It's very persuasive.

"Where are you then?" I glanced outside. There was a mist and a weak sun and a squirrel on the lawn. Lawn? that's a laugh, I thought, and wrote MOWER on the A – D.

"I'm in a village just off the motorway," he said. "I can see you from where I am, I believe." I pulled the altar-cloth a bit tighter. I had ideas about finishing the embroidery myself, as I lazed through the summer under the mulberry tree, the lush wine-coloured fruit falling into my open mouth. But now it slipped, clinging by the gold thread rather scratchily to one shoulder and modestly concealing my knees.

"OK," I said brightly. "Just give me five minutes to finish what we were doing." It sounded distinctly odd, but the "we" was crafty. I wanted to give the impression of a large household, not just one of us who took hours to answer the phone.

I dragged on clean jeans and a tee shirt, ran a comb through my hair. I used a darkish lipstick I usually hate but which might throw the rest of my face into relief (instead of the ashcan where it belongs at 7 a.m.) and distract attention from everywhere else. Then I heard the car coming up the drive.

On the way to the front door I picked up a tennis racquet. Well, it's a game you don't play alone even if you have a court which we hadn't. At least, not one that was playable on. I swung it meaningfully as I opened the front door.

He was even better than his voice. Not quite as gorgeous as the dogs he led towards me, and a fraction less than the old American drophead coupé left at an angle which showed its thirty-ish lines, like a model in a bikini shot from below to avoid the wrong idea about her droops. But I did rather wish the dogs were leaving *him* for a few weeks.

We both smiled. He glanced at the racquet and said, "So that's what you were doing?"

I dropped it like a hot potato and shook back my hair. A small bone fell out at my feet. Bustle had a way of hiding her treasures in my underwear but this was going too far.

"Bob and Bill," the man said, introducing the dogs. It was a nice change from those long, boring, unpronounceable tags they use in Kennel Club circles for any dog which isn't just somebody's much-loved pet. I ventured a respectful pat apiece. The two long, elegant heads drew back, the great liquid eyes implored me not to disarrange the exquisite coiffures. Their attractive owner added, "And I'm Ross Washington." He held out a hand. It was big and square, and if I'd been a palmist I'd have said his life, long or short, would be best spent with me.

"Come in," I said, "the game can wait." I meant tennis but it sounded loaded with meaning. I only made it worse by adding, "I do love to play before breakfast." He raised one eyebrow. I decided to change the subject.

"We're just about to make some coffee," I said graciously, confident he was rushing to catch that plane and would therefore refuse. "Like some?" But he nodded and smiled and to my horror followed me into the big untidy kitchen with the falling plaster and brown paper counselling.

"Find a chair" I invited. It wasn't easy. They were all hidden by dogs.

He perched on the edge of the table while I got down six mugs and lined them up busily, for all the world as if I expected the local tennis team to come bounding in. He looked OK but you can't tell a rapist by his squint. Some of them, I bet, have blue eyes, tanned skin, hair the colour of a badger's brush and a laugh like the motor on a mixer when its flipped its lid. I shook in some coffee and added boiling water to all the mugs as we chatted about the weather. I passed one of the mugs to his corner of the table and shoved Rosie out of the carver.

"Flying where?" I asked, indicating the vacated seat with a nod of my head. I noticed a few stray hairs but it was too late to brush them away first. I really would have to tighten up on organisation. Get a room ready to receive customers; buy coffee beans; use cups. And wear a bra *every* day instead of just when going into town. And to hang a trilby hat in the hall.

"New York, home."

I said automatically, as one does when anyone is about to risk their all going into the unknown. "Lucky old you!" and edged him the sugar.

"Why?" Bob and Bill had crumpled up together like twin parachutes from a great height, slowly and breeze-blown. They lay in a heap on the floor, always elegant and beautiful. My own three dogs sat bolt upright resenting the afghans' advantages, like council school kids faced with Etonians. Class war springs up in small pockets of insecurity everywhere.

I said, "Well, isn't New York where the action is?" It sounded so right when I was saying it and so wrong when it was said. I flinched from my own reflexes.

He looked round the room and grinned. "Quite a bit right here, I guess," he said, doing the Americanese naturally. "Who wants action, anyway?"

"I do." The four spare mugs of coffee steamed downwind slowly. As he finished his, I absently passed him another and took a second myself. I'd forgotten the tennis team altogether.

"Well," he said, "I don't. This is where I'd rather be. Right here."

Upstairs I could hear Willy and Teddy waiting for morning prayers, perhaps. Or another round of Tossing the Chocky Drop. They were giving short urgent barks and it sounded as though they were shuffling round my room with boots on. Mattie stretched suddenly and went outside, passing the afghans with head down and eyes averted, mediocrity passing majesty. Her embarrassment was only equalled by my own. Why should anyone prefer this monstrous mausoleum of Victoriana to some slick chick in a New York apartment, all air-conditioning, central heating and Venetian blinds?

I said, "Nice to be back home, though. See the family, and all." I flinched as I lapsed even further into Deep South. But he just said, "No family. Service apartment, shady side of the block." And then silence. We glanced at the dogs. They sorted themselves into huge brown eyes and anguish at being in such unsavoury surroundings. Afghans recognise a part to play in every new scene, they over-act like mad and thoroughly enjoy any big build-up of drama, and this was a great opportunity. A couple of real ham roles those two played, with Bob in the lead every time.

"You must be just crazy about dogs," said Ross Washington admiringly, "or would that be a handicap in your work?" He was ready for his third mug.

"You can't *like* what you're doing in a job like this," I said. "You have to be fanatical about it – so that you cry when you read about a dead dodo."

He laughed and suddenly it wasn't really at all like a mixer with a flipped lid, and his shiny teeth were all of a piece without gold or gap. Overhead the noise had stopped. The silence was more worrying than the activity, but I put it firmly from my mind. There was a time for everything and this moment could mark a twist in life, fate and – what seemed more important just then – possible monotony.

When he finally got up to leave there was slight tension and six empty coffee mugs on the table. We stood together at the porch and I thought for a moment he might give me just one brief kiss to keep with me when I was on my own again. It would satisfy some of those passing fancies, like an iced lolly instead of a chocolate walnut sundae during a diet. I'm nobody's nympho, but I'm not an ice lolly either. Funny how one's mind runs on food as a substitute for sex. Maybe that accounts for dogs and their precious bones. But both Ross and I recognised the proprieties – as people do most of the time except in fiction – and the empty air vibrated with what might have been, which had, admittedly, a certain wistful attraction of its own.

Bob and Bill took no interest whatsoever in what might be going on. Bob was black with dark mournful eyes, and Bill amber and black with a very aristocratic nose, slightly tilted at the end, suggesting disdain. Nothing less than early elevation into the peerage would have been suitable homage. They took their meals in the dining-room under the polished oval table with its brass claw feet. They had a curious way of lying down to eat in a leisurely way I have never seen done by any other dog. The rest of the time they spent in the conservatory, stretched full length on wickerwork chairs lined with cushions dating from the old days of the Empire.

I spent some time cleaning up the conservatory, disposing of potted palms scorched dead from a succession of summers. The scrubbed floor turned out to be mosaic, with occasional flashes of kingfisher blue and sunset flame. The acres of glass glowed after a spray with the garden hose and a final polish. The hall was clear and cool. It merely needed cleaning and some plants for the long marble-topped console; the old crocodile skin looked good down the centre. Redecorating could wait. I hung framed maps, illustrated poetry, military scrolls and awards, Victorian Sunday School Attendance certificates, class reports and illuminated addresses. My daughter had once said rather dryly that it made the place look like an Underground Station, but it did offer something to study while waiting for the next burst of activity.

Upstairs my bedroom boasted french doors leading on to a balcony where at first I saw myself as Amanda from *Private Lives*, but now recognised more clearly the mat-shaker who tossed dog hairs into the begonias. My bed was eight feet square and at least two hundred years old and reputed to have slept innumerable queens and their companions. It was known in the family as "The Playground" but was fast becoming Teddy's and Willy's and Bustle's.

The weather was too good to spend emptying packing-cases. I was even glad to see Humphrey when he brought the letters. It got me legitimately outside. I was leaning against the wrought-iron rose-covered archway when he arrived in the late afternoon the next day. There had been no sign of a sheikh and no sign of anyone else either, except Mrs Flutey.

Mrs Flutey was a bit deaf. She wore a hearing aid, and her glasses hung on a cord, but from what I could discover neither did much for her because she never listened to a word I said and never looked at whatever we spoke about.

She arrived after a phone call to say she was on her way. "I'm coming," she announced, as if into battle. "Whereabouts are you? I shall find you. What are your fees? Maribou eats nothing – but nothing. We have appetites like birds. I can't see what you can charge as she merely wants water, just a drink. That's Maribou. Goodbye."

Then she was at the door. A small thin lady, younger than I would have guessed, with sharp features and a narrow mouth which opened and shut like a beak. Maribou was a Maltese terrier.

Mrs Flutey said, "Here she is. I can't stay. Do make sure she doesn't get cod-liver-oil on her beard. Watch her motions. Clip her claws. Tidy her eyes. Have you a proper renal thermometer? Never mind, try her ear. Swab her nostrils. Trim her tail-end, saves sluicing. You've lost a tile. Gravel needs laying. What a view! Pity, that motorway. Back on Thursday the 14th . . ."

But she didn't go. She came in after me, nose alert as a pointer's. I offered her tea but she shook her head while inspecting the range, ran her finger along the mantelpiece, her toe along the fender, her eyes along the dresser. Then she said, "Oil the doors. Lemon's good. You're not very tidy, are you?" She peered at Maribou, and added, "Blue rinse" but more to herself than me. Then she walked to the door, cried, "That's it then," and went.

I forgot everything she told me, asked me, advised me. Maribou was pretty, dainty and spotlessly clean. She had a bland expression and was utterly composed and self-sufficient. Very cuddly, but allowing little by way of affection. I put her basket in the conservatory with Bob and Bill and she took up residence after a bit of fussing with the blanket, cushion and small, woolly hat which I thought at first was for nightwear, but turned out to be Mrs Flutey's, though whether she left it for Maribou, thus showing a chink in the armour of her severe practicality, or by mistake, showing another in her impressive efficiency, I never knew.

Humphrey brought a letter from my husband detailing the rigours of hospital food and other deprivations. He added, "I can't tell you the *truth* on the phone as they might easily intercept the letter and *take reprisals*," as if he were in a prison camp. I think he really believed it could happen. He also put, "Sister (you know which I mean) has a wig! The cap caught on Mick Lafferty's traction and both fell in the bedpan together (cap and wig, not Lafferty and Sister!). No one dared to laugh. She now wears a curly red one and looks like Coco the Clown." But not a word about his health. Before we spoke on the phone that evening I tried to make some enquiries.

"Good evening. I would like to speak to someone about my husband in Frimley Ward."

"You would like *what*?"

"Someone in charge of my husband." It made him sound like a homicidal maniac. I added hastily, "Someone reliable." I meant someone in authority. I was getting harrassed.

There was a short pause. "Everyone here is thoroughly reliable," warned the voice, now as stiff and cold as a corpse. It reminded me of my doctor's receptionist when I rang in frantic appeal because Pa had collapsed with a heart attack. She had said in exactly the same way, "The doctor is very busy," as if he couldn't possibly be interrupted painting the ceiling for anything less than Black Death running riot among the masses.

"I'm sure everyone's quite fantastic," I assured her. "I mean, could I have a word with . . ." but she had gone away, fuming.

I held on and on. Then I cut off, fuming too. I just had to accept they were going to hold out on me with news unless I turned up to grovel for it. Maybe, I thought, I'll write one of my Letters. They get written to shops who sell me short, services that let me down, and professions who scorn my right as a fee-paying customer. The letters begin, "Dear Sirs, As a journalist preparing a series of articles on comparative values/specific cases of outrageous inconsideration/disparity in simple justice . . . etc" and it usually scares them into immediate attention and explanation, if not actual restitution. If it doesn't, my second letter begins, "Dear Sirs, In my role of journalist I now propose to use our current disagreement, and your subsequent refusal to acknowledge fault, in a newspaper feature which I shall entitle . . ." and then go to ask for a few relevant details (ever so nicely) such as how many thousand other customers have had to fight to get even the tiniest hope of recognition. Ah! the Power of the Press. I never did have to go further than the two letters before the matter was hurriedly investigated, at the very least.

I usually wrote to the Customer Relations Officer, or General Manager or even Managing Director, after everyone else passed me over. I once got in touch with the Company Chairman when a new television set developed a series of rabid distortions after only ten days. The supplier virtually gave up and said he thought long noses and pointed toes were being worn on BBC I this winter. Players, on stage and field, ran briskly into the wings or offside like ink runs tipped on paper, leaving the original blot where it was. It was only funny the first time. My letters began after the seventeenth occurrence and, I was told bad reception could be due to local conditions. I rang the Managing Director but, like the rest of the company, he was, they said, at sea. So I wrote to the Chairman and marked the envelope HIGHLY PERSONAL!

He not only replied but suggested a meeting. He gave me sherry from his drink cabinet, lunch at the Savoy and a brand new television set after his own men had inspected mine and found it was just as bad as I said it was.

The letter to the hospital was a mite more respectful. I couldn't risk any revenge on the patient. It was never so much as acknowledged, but at least it helped me feel better about the situation. I entrusted the letter to Humphrey, who used his good eye on the envelope while the plastic version rested lightly on me. One grew used to it but never happy with it, like taxation.

To distract myself, I said, "Lovely day. Bet we're in for a super summer."

"See that bird there?" He moved his head towards his left shoulder. I followed his ear.

"No," I said.

"'tis a Willy Warbler. Wot you probably calls a Great Tit."

I'd never called anyone such a thing in my life. I protested. "Oh, really, no. I'm sure you're wrong."

"Never, Miss, never. I've been spotting Great Tits since I were a lad. I know one when I sees one. And that 'un means a spell o' frost, sure as I'm a Collie." I looked at him. By no stretch of the imagination could he be – but of course, it was probably his surname. Also a challenge. I had to retaliate.

"Well," I said amiably, "we'll see. Personally, I saw a Pickled Hedgehog this morning and *that* means a heatwave, sure as I'm a looney!"

Which, of course, just goes to show, because the heatwave began next morning . . .

Colonel Pelmett was due at tea time. He had been very military on the phone, barking, albeit politely, with a voice of firm authority about his dog. He would be over, he said, with his Rover at four sharp. I couldn't be sure whether he referred to his dog or his car and even when he arrived, it could have been either.

The Colonel was staggeringly typical of any television Army officer over middle-age. White hair and whiskers. So upright you could hear bugles. I felt my own muscles draw to attention and wished he were around a lot more often to keep my figure under control. A very old dog followed him.

"Rover!" announced the Colonel after introducing himself. The old dog glanced up and wagged his tail.

"Sit!" demanded the Colonel. It was a pity he had such badly-fitting dentures which made him shush his 's's. The way it came out quite startled me.

Rover sat, luckily understanding the correct interpretation.

"A camel-hound," claimed the Colonel, proudly, but defying argument.

"Gracious!" I said impressed. "I've never even heard of one."

The Colonel glanced at me suspiciously to see his word wasn't being held in doubt. It certainly wasn't. If there really are desert cats and pyramid cats, then why not camel-hounds? I've never been further east than Felixstowe, but I'm gullible as good-night.

"Do come in," I suggested, holding the door wide.

"Hup!" he snapped. A man of few words and it was a pity he shot them all like darts because only a look of sympathy from Rover himself stopped me leaping away on the command. "Rush job," said the Colonel. "Wittering." I nodded sagely. Not for me to ask what kind of a rush job that was. Let him witter where he would.

He went back to the car and disgorged a severe-looking box bed lined with clean copies of *The Times* (no blankets in this battalion – none of your softie-soldier stuff) and two bowls, one marked DOG, the other WATER. There was a small hard ball for exercise, nothing else.

"Sleeps anywhere," said the Colonel. He was behind me, but as I turned to face him, he and the dog exchanged looks and the old man's face softened. His pale eyes were suffused with love. "Inside, if possible," he added gruffly.

"Of course," I agreed, dismissing the kennels once again. "We do have a nice cosy kitchen. Well, not too warm," I corrected myself quickly.

"One meal a day, access to water." He paused. "A bit of exercise."

"As much as he needs," I said softly. The old dog looked as if he needed rest a great deal more. I picked up the ball. "Will he catch it?" I asked, as if it were a measle. The Colonel again looked stern. He took the ball from me and unscrewed it round the middle. Inside were some red pills.

"One a day," he muttered, ashamed of weakness in the camp. "A bit of a heart . . ."

He paused and the eyes were anxious. "Won't take his medicine like a man. Have to get them out of this thing. Seems to associate a ball as OK because of the days we played cricket together."

I bent down and patted Rover and saw at close quarters, the greying hairs, the loose muzzle. "He's not so young," I ventured. "Poor old boy." His master gave me a long look. The same could have been said about him. I felt sorry for both of them.

"Seventeen," he claimed defiantly. "Known 'em live to twenty or more in the Punjab. Why, the Fifteenth Foot had a basenji in the Mess, outlived the lot of 'em. Name of Dumbo, I remember. Must have been all of twenty-seven when he went missing." He glared at me, daring me to disbelieve. "Rover came to us as a six-week pup. Worships the wife. Chums we are . . ." He allowed himself a smile. "He won't go yet awhile." He was trying to delude himself, desperately scared he could be wrong. I thought how wildly Wittering must be calling to part such lovers.

"Don't worry," I pleaded, "I'll keep him well for you, I promise." I meant, of course, 'I'll keep him alive for you' but I couldn't say that. I couldn't even be sure of doing it really. If the old dog fretted for his master, it could be too much stress for the heart to bear.

"Back soon, boy," muttered the Colonel, clearing his throat twice. He stuck his hands in his pockets. It was so out of character I knew he must be moved beyond even the customary rigid self-discipline.

Rover awkwardly and painfully drew himself to his feet again, waiting for a last caress. It hurt me to see the effort he made, the pleading eyes. But the Colonel hesitated, chin up, and for just a moment some unspoken message passed between them. Then he turned and walked away, back to the car. I knew that one touch and he might have given up, given in, forsaken Wittering and his iron will with it. He never looked back and the car moved down the drive and out through the gate on to the road.

Rover and I were left, looking after him, wondering.

The box bed had been put down in the middle of the kitchen. Rover stood by it, a new recruit waiting for kit inspection. Treacle strolled over and spoke in a low, but kindly rumble. She might have been Matron welcoming the latest patient to the Geriatric Ward. Treacle would have made a superb Matron. Firm, but with strict rules about protocol and nothing too much trouble on behalf of her inmates. No one else was ever allowed under my chair in the kitchen. Next to it, yes. Behind it, OK. Even *on* it when I wasn't. But *under* it, certainly not.

Rover clambered into the box and lay down with a sigh. He was, I could see, panting and shaky and for the first time I registered a mounting panic. What on earth was I doing? Plants wither, unmourned. People get rushed off to hospital and become the business of others, but beloved pets would remain for me to protect and I was well aware that in most cases they mattered more than a crop, and sometimes, indeed, even more than a relative.

"Look," I explained, "I'll have to move you round a bit or I'm going to fall over that box all the time." I bent to drag it towards the wall under the window. Rover growled. Ever so slightly, even apologetically, but enough to show disapproval. For obvious reasons, that place, facing the door and dead centre of the entrance, was considered now his to occupy till his master came to fetch him home again. Rover had no doubt at all that his master would be back, such was the understanding between them, and he meant to keep watch and be ready with the earliest possible welcome.

So I left him there. What was a bit of inconvenience for a while? I filled his water bowl and left it within reach, another obstacle in what was growing to be an assault course. But anything was tolerable to keep Rover happy.

I remembered I had to ring Adam's mother about Lady. Adam had arrived the night before, near to tears. Mrs Hollingbury, he said, was packing his case to go back to school two days before half-term ended. Mummy was still away following a long weekend with friends, and he dared not leave Lady at home with no one to see she was all right. They both looked at me with such appeal that all I could do was bring out the ginger snaps and conclude the deal at 20p a week (Adam had again offered the entire wealth of his pocket money but we finally agreed to split it 20/30) until the summer holidays, and meantime I would speak to Mummy when she came back.

Lady settled in immediately. She seemed extremely happy. Peering through her thick bead curtaining of heavy fringe, she showed bright eager eyes and black squab nose, like a pickled walnut, damp and twitchy. Her rear end wagged cheerfully. It seemed sad that only away from home was she able to find freedom. Of course she missed Adam, but she wasn't the only dog to convince me that their seventh sense reassured them of returning owners.

I tried Adam's home number that morning, as soon as the Colonel had gone. And spoke to Mrs Hollingbury. She was calm, polite, a trifle distant, and she said Adam's mother, Mrs Adair, was expected back in a few days. Meantime, could she take a message? help in any way? I thought it best not to mention Lady.

She took my number. Mrs Adair would ring me when she had a moment, and if it was a contribution to a village function, we could rely on her generosity.

But not on her maternal responsibilities, I thought savagely.

Lady was the perfect guest. Unobtrusive, undemanding, enjoying corn flakes or caviare. Only when the phone rang she did a complete Jekyll and Hyde: she leapt in the air with a blood-curdling shriek and dived for the phone, usually knocking over a chum or two, anything else in her way, and me. It took a week to calm her into merely alerting instead of attacking. I did it by pushing a ginger snap into her jaws the moment they opened for the initial war-cry: then after my first few surprise counter-offensives, I threw it so her attention was averted to catching, and finally I offered a piece as I went to answer the phone; eventually, we were down to a 'good girl' murmur as she sat, ears pricked, attention on the biscuit tin. It was unorthodox but effective.

Thunder always worried her, but so it did many of the others. Together and quivering, there would be a lot of sneaking under tables and chairs, back to boxes. One, I remember, would push its head under the blanket. Maribou, alone of any dog I ever knew, loved a storm, and literally danced as lightning lit up the room. She had no fear of anything, but perhaps after living with Mrs Flutey, this was understandable.

The only time sneezing upset Lady was when it was me sneezing, so I made a great effort to avert the problem. She seemed to associate it with a last gasp or the death rattle or some fatal warning and from anyone she barely knew, she didn't care.

The afghans lazed and looked beautiful: Rover watched the door and dreamed of his master's return. Teddy made the best of things and joined Treacle in Good Works, welcoming newcomers and pointing out to me, rather plaintively, when the water bowl was running dry. Willy watched Rosie stalking tigers in the daffodils – but from a safe distance – and the others sparred a bit or worried the hearth-rug to while away the time, much as Montmorency idled with the teaspoons while waiting for the trip to begin with Jerome K. Jerome in his unforgettable story of *Three Men in a Boat*.

We were a contented little commune for the moment, presided over by me and Mattie, frivolled by Frilly. It seemed that for a space of time snatched from eternity everything was going to be all right.

7

You never really know much about anything. I thought of putting that in chalk on the wall, only it held too much gloom. The phone rang the following morning and I lurched from toast and marmalade out of complacency and into problems.

I was trying to work out how best to fortify myself against starvation. With a strict sense of responsibility, I knew I could never leave my precious charges unguarded while I was out – nor the silver christening spoon. Not even to fetch ginger snaps and pigs' heads. Glancing through the invaluable local paper I found a fascinating small ad. which read, quite frankly, "THROATS . . . our prices most competitive. Try us for HEARTS, LUNGS AND PAUNCHES." It sounded like a distribution centre for transplants. Further on, after "Deliveries in your area" and "Strictly for cash", it said, "Ring the Pet & Pussy Pantry" with an exchange number about seven miles away.

I rang. It was the "Deliveries in your area" I liked.

I was told the PPP van came out my way on Fridays and they would certainly call. Yes, they had dog meal and their own wholewheat and charcoal Rewards. But, she coaxed coyly, they would tempt me with a variety of exciting things when they arrived! She made it sound like the Waldorf on Wheels. I said I'd try and control my excitement till they got here, and went back to the trotters which were daintily pointing toes from a pan of pork gravy. I still had two crates of tinned dog food and a couple of jumbo-sized containers of dog meal and biscuit.

Just as it dawned on me that I had nothing at all for myself, the phone rang. It was Sister Maude.

"We were wondering whether you would be coming in to see your husband today?" It was almost a command. I steeled myself.

"No," I said. "Why? Is he worse?"

Grudgingly, she admitted he was quite a lot better. It was a very difficult situation for her: if she said he was worse it might reflect on her management, and if she said he was better, I could hardly be summoned to come at once. "He's doing very nicely," she agreed. Doing what? He never did a thing *nicely* – neither his work, nor me, nor the handle repairs to the fridge door. He did things enthusiastically, efficiently, reluctantly, deliciously, often successfully, sometimes rather badly. A man of amusing and endearing extremes. Remembering that, I began to feel frustrated again and very very lonely. It made me a bit abrasive.

"Well," I said briskly, "I'm glad to hear that, of course. But he's in such good hands. And I'm so far away, it's impossible to get there, so . . ."

She interrupted, "Have you a sitter problem?"

It sounded like piles or something. I echoed, "Sitter?"

"A kiddie question, then?"

I closed my eyes. "No," I said. "Well, yes, in a way. But not kiddies. Dogs."

There was a short pause. Then she said coldly, "I would have thought that, for a sick husband, you could have left a dog." Her contempt spelt the word as R A T.

"Look, I didn't say *dog*. I said *dogs*. Lots of dogs. Other people's dogs. My income, food, rates. I can't leave them, any more than your patients could be left. Not unless it's a case of Life and Death in Frimley Ward. And even then . . ."

I stopped to glance at Rover. He was trembling ever so slightly. I muttered to myself ". . . and it's more likely to be here!" But she was the sort who believes in either/or.

She said, "Your husband is only just recovering from a severe attack, you know." I knew. I had been the one with him when he was at his worst. I said so and she made disapproving noises.

"Look," I said again, as if I were showing her the pimple on my elbow, "he hates being visited. He always says he feels at such a disadvantage in bed. Well, not *always*, of course. . . . He enjoys displaying nobility, tolerance and self-sacrifice much more than knowing I can claim it after a three-and-a-half hour journey to sit half way under the bed for an hour." On my last visit, luckily behind drawn curtains, they had brought me a chair – so we could hold hands and exchange lingering glances, I suppose. Only I don't know where they found the chair because it was so low that when I sat down I disappeared from sight and he thought I'd gone home. I wasn't permitted to sit on the bed, and standing about like a spare tick in the bedding, made us both uneasy. I went on, "We phone and write all the time and . . ." But why was I having to defend myself? I added, "Then there's the christening spoon and things. One awkward kiss over the Lucozade won't make up for bankruptcy!"

OK, so I exaggerated a bit. Some people tell lies, others sneer, most boast. We all have our weapons of defence. Mine's verbal embroidery. She said, giving in or up (I wasn't sure which), "Oh, well, you know best, I suppose. I'd better tell you, however – we're moving him tomorrow."

"There now," I said placatingly, "you were able to say it on the phone just as easily as in your office." Then I squealed, "Not *home*?" in such horror she must have had her suspicions confirmed about me having a lover in the closet. Not home, though! Not yet, not with so much undone and so much done the wrong way and so much to do! It couldn't be home! But I was suddenly terrified it would be home . . .

"Convalescence and a continuation of the specialised treatment with observation at our coastal clinic," she said primly. "We think it best for him to be there a few weeks depending on response and progress." She was gloating because I was excluded, and I was thanking God for a sensible let-out. Patient and Rover competing for exclusive dying rights? It was unthinkable.

"We would like you to bring a few things for him to take," she tried again firmly. Did she mean asprins and cough mixture?

I poised a pencil over the letter from an Inland Revenue official calmly threatening death by firing-squad behind guarded words.

"Of course," I agreed because I was fed up with fencing. "Such as what?"

"Well . . ." For once she was at a bit of a loss. "I suggest some shirts, of course. Those he has here are hardly suitable." What could she mean? "Hankies and hosiery." "Underwear. He'll need a lot to last him six weeks at the sea!" I remembered a woman who once worked for my mother when I was a kid who said she never took a holiday because the sea air rotted the larynx. Could that apply to Y-fronts and socks? "Anything else?"

Sister Maude said suspiciously, "What time will you be coming, then?"

It was a time for surprise tactics. "I'm not sure. I'll be speaking to him on the phone this afternoon or tomorrow. I don't ring during the evening because of the television."

"Really . . ." She began indignant again, but I interrupted, "Not *mine*. I don't even have one at the moment. *Yours*. He gets ratty if I keep him away from the Weather or Westerns. And downright dangerous if he misses any explicit sex scenes necessary for the development of the plot!"

She ignored it. "Then we shan't be able to have A Talk?" She sighed.

"Considering I never was able to find anyone in authority willing to spare me a few minutes when I *did* come in," I countered, "I'm sure it won't matter."

It was a nasty jab to end with but if he were leaving Frimley Ward, we need not fear repercussions. There wouldn't be much chance now to spike his cold semolina with something from the poison cupboard. And it was true. They were always much too busy to speak to me when *I* was desperate.

I never have been a nurse-worshipper. They're people, like us, but these days you wouldn't think many of them are people. They've joined the ranks of the Me-Firsters and at one hospital, a year earlier, my husband had suffered miserable deprivations by staff on strike who even refused to let others help their patients. Nice girls, who would have rushed to do their best for someone collapsing in the street, stood by prepared to let anything happen in the hospital. It did nothing to improve relations either side of the bedpan.

The crying I did back in the kitchen was for me and Rover and the loose plaster rather than for my husband who was better, comfortable and wouldn't have a worry in the world until the six weeks' sea air was over. And then, and then . . . was he going to find a few worries here!

Crying, like making, and falling into, love, leaves me hungry. I rooted about but there was nothing except dog food and limp Marie Osbornes. I remembered the Pets Pantryman would be on his way soon, and that someone would be in with a miniature Manchester terrier called Marmalade, who had worms. The future looked shaky. I felt sodden with self-pity. I wished I Drank.

Suppose no more customers arrived? Ought I to arrange for a new notice-board to go up in the space at the gate with, maybe, something bigger up on the Motorway? Something like "LEAVE YOUR LOVED ONE AT THE HOLLIES"? Only it sounded far too much like internment than a home substitute. If I made it "LEAVE YOUR LOVED ONE AT THE HOLLIES HOLIDAY HOME FOR DOGS" it would be clearer but at the speed they hared down the outside lane they'd probably never get any further than the first four words before shooting off across the central reservation. How about "HOLLIES HOLIDAY HOME FOR DOGS"? But HOLLIES sounded prickly, wintry, uncomfortable. I'd just make it "HOLIDAY HOME FOR DOGS". Working it all out took away the self-pity and the tears. I meandered through a mug or two of coffee with Mattie lying on my feet and Teddy sitting with Rover. Treacle was taking time off from her vigil there to have a stroll outside. The rest were placid, relaxed, contented. Things were really not too bad, after all. I began to write it all in a letter to my husband . . .

When the phone rang and a man asked if I could manage a boxer for the weekend, I gave a nervous giggle and said I could hardly wait.

We were back to normal.

8

And then Willy had a fit.

I had made up my mind to dash into the village for food. Many a prehistoric man must have felt as I did when hunger threatened the tribe. I decided to shut the dogs in the rooms where they had their beds, water and friends, take the car for the last time, and load up as if for a siege, of course being careful to bow to the house as I left. My mother had always turned at the front gate, and bowed to the home she was leaving behind for an hour or two, confident nothing could then happen to it while she was gone. And it never did!

The sun was breaking through after a night of cloud but little rain. The day was right for a risk. I would not wear the green jeans, which were clean. I would only cross over on utterly deserted roads. I would steer clear of shop blinds (my aunt was once hit by one which fell down into the middle of the afternoon and concussed her into marrying a man who sang alto in the choir and pushed spring onions up his nose for catarrh), together with scaffolding and precipices. I wasn't afraid for myself, mark you, but I was terrified for the dogs.

I got dressed with the balcony doors open, thinking what bliss it all really was – in a modest sort of way. I was thinking how humans, from earliest times, had found a dog the best substitute for the rare right companion. Maybe, I thought, if everyone had a pet of their own, issued like army rations in wartime, to love and to care for, the entire direction of humanity might be put back on the right course.

Teddy was on the balcony, ears through the railings, alert for marauders below. Maribou and Bustle curled happily together like some huge cushion of swansdown. I was about to hurry on down to Rover, always my first concern, when Willy gave a little strangled sound and began shivering. The shivering grew intense, then it gave way to sudden collapse, complete and uncontrollable. I thought she was dead, but the shivering and jerking went on . . .

I rushed across and held her in my arms, but she was unresponsive. Her mouth was half open. Saliva trickled on to my sleeve. I was frantic. In that one moment, all the responsibilities and problems of this new financial undertaking were revealed for the monstrosity they were. I lay Willy gently on the bed and rushed to the phone. I kept very calm. I had to give my new vet the impression of level-headedness in crises. Taking the rough-haired with the smooth-coated. I was brief, cool, unemotional. I dazzled and amazed myself. Sometimes I do . . .

The vet said, "It's a fit".

"Of course," I replied, as if I'd known all the time. I had to hang on to the phone because I was shaking like an old banger on a cart-track.

"Did the owner warn you?"

"No," I said, "the dog was just left by someone else."

She said gently, "Look, don't worry." Who said I was worried? So my mouth *was* dry, my throat ached and I trembled as if palsied. But who said I was worried?

I said casually, "Anything I can do about it?" Such as ask Teddy to get down on his knees and have a word with God for us?

"Not really. She should come round in a moment and be perfectly OK. Would you like me to drop in and see her this morning?"

"Might be best," I agreed. If she hadn't suggested, I would have insisted.

"You'll be in?" I would never take one single step outside again. Willy was lying quite still, breathing, but otherwise as dead a dog as I ever saw.

"I'll be in all right," I assured her. And then suddenly, the serenity and calm quiet confidence crumpled. "Do please come soon. I'm terrified she's going to do something even more dramatic, like dying?"

She laughed. "There won't be anything like that until I get there. They dare not! She may be epileptic. It happens. But she'll perk up in a minute. Keep her cool and quiet and make sure she has a bowl of water handy. Let her sleep if she wants to."

"Hang on a second," I said, and put down the phone. I went over and knelt by Willy's inert body. She opened her eyes and wagged her tail feebly. I put my face on her curly coat and tears suffused it like boiling water on tripe. Then I rushed back.

"She seems better already, but please do come in as soon as you can." Blow the expense, I thought. Rates wait: the Willys of this world sometimes make a dash into the next.

"I'll be with you in an hour or so. I have to pick up a few things first."

A few things could have meant food . . . shopping. My stomach was shouting for help and nudging me in the empty ribs.

"I hate to ask, but starvation takes precedence over protocol, I believe. Could you bring me a loaf or two and maybe some sausages?" It sounded like an order for a parable.

Later, when I brought her some cereals and milk, Willy was looking apologetic. She wagged her stumpy bobble tail and smiled. I hugged her. The others had gone out and she was in her basket in the shadow of the curtains near the window. The day was growing very hot.

"Right," I said, "let's try not to do that again, shall we?" She sat up and stretched. Then she yawned. She lapped up the last of the Weetabix and finished the milk. She'd already downed enough water to fill a bath tub.

The others strolled in and out unconcerned, except for bossy Bustle who felt it necessary to come over and check. Bustle would have felt she was missing out being kept back from a bomb disposal unit.

I went downstairs, limp with relief. Frilly was with Rover, snuggled between his paws. She was a kitten of little caution. Her nine lives were up for a new lease. She enjoyed being where the action was and when there was no action she often pushed her luck a bit. But Rover liked company: one eye was open, one old paw resting lightly across the kitten's back. It was his turn to be protective again.

I heard a car draw away as I walked into the kitchen. It was impossible to hear the bell when I was upstairs and I was horrified I might have missed the Pets' Pantryman. For all I knew, I could have let this week's throats disappear into the distance. I flung open the back door and nearly strangled an Irish wolfhound. It was tied by its lead to the handle. The poor thing, almost as big as me, was jerked off his feet so suddenly that we met with considerable force. I was the one that fell over.

For a moment I went on sitting there, with him towering over me.

"Who the hell are you?" I asked angrily. He had grey hair, grizzled like an old bear the Mounties couldn't catch. He had legs almost unnaturally straight, and a taut concise body with a utility tail. No afghan flow nor apso fringe. His head was spare and dauntingly beautiful.

Enormous dark eyes stared at me. I got up. Enormous white teeth were bared at me. I got well away. A note was leaning against the dead fir tree in the disintegrating tub.

It read, "In great haste. Please take care of Toby and the Angel. Will try and ring from airport. If not, back 29th. Many thanks", and it was signed R. Shane.

There was no sign of any angel and I know I'd have noticed. One can turn a blind eye to a lurking demon, but not an angel. I turned the page and read, "One meal a day, large" – well, that went without saying. "Could he Die for the Clan, just to keep his hand in, sometimes please?" I suppose it's something one has to keep fresh in one's mind, to be ready for Action over the Border. I didn't know whether to be annoyed or amused. But anger draws the face down, laughter up. There's no choice when you're over forty.

So I grinned and, just to see what would happen, said "Die for the Clan, Toby." He stared at me. Then he shut his mouth tight with disapproval and sat down.

It wasn't what I expected but maybe it was what he'd been taught. Maybe it just meant that death was defeat, and we weren't having any of that. I mean, symbolic. I just didn't know. But with the fierce pride of the Irish, it was just possible. Mattie, now, could drop dead on command, but then she was an Old *English* sheepdog and it could be said that we Sassenachs are best at graceful surrender.

Orders and commands are a reflex action to dogs, more than understanding or intelligence. Maybe the smart dog is the one who doesn't come when he's called, or, like Rosie when told to fetch a thrown stick, rushes off on her own business and eventually brings back a very dead and smelly vole for her own purposes. I know some dogs are said to love Obedience work, but watching them looking craven At Heel, and sniffing anxiously round to find the right linen square, reminds me far too much of Fascism in the late thirties. Prisoners in an exercise yard. Toeing the Line to Pass the Winning Post First. The fact they do it to please someone they love makes it worse. How *can* someone they love demand so much? Risk their suffering a sense of failure? The one thing animals have left, since we domesticated them for our own reasons, is freedom from competition. And now we try and take that, too. Mattie, of course, had been taught by her previous owners. I never embarrassed her. No dog I ever owned would be so lacking in commonsense that he felt it necessary to waste time on performing silly tricks, anyway.

The sun was shimmering on the tarmacadam along the Motorway. Another hot day, setting light to the buttercups. I looked across to the beautiful timber kennels, creamy-pale and immaculate: the ample runs, the shiny chrome link fencing. The emptiness. It would, I thought ruefully, have looked even better with orderly occupants. It wasn't that I grudged a share of eiderdown. I never have. I like company. I needed company. It just seemed a pity and I do so hate waste. I began to wonder what I could put there to fill the spaces . . .

Cars streamed towards the coast. Friday was the day the traffic went in the reverse direction, more of the population heading seawards than to work. In a thousand homes, someone would be saying, "Come on, Dave, you never take a day off – well, only for

Fulham mid-week when they're at home. What? Well, that was important. You had to. I might have had one of my depressions if you hadn't. Let's go to the beach. Give the kids a day off, too. Oh, come on! They don't pay you *that* much: this is clerk's perks. Everyone does it now and then. I mean, it's common practice. They can't do anything, the Union see to that. I'll be ready in half an hour. Get Robby's sandshoes, will you? Under the stairs and, I say, see if you can find . . ." And there goes a bit more productivity.

I remembered doing the same myself when the kids were young, before they left home starry-eyed in the arms of others less ambitious for them than we were. And now they came home with the stars diminished and older than either of us.

Hetty Hebditch's car climbed the lane towards the house. It was smart and bright, shiny and new, sporty and open. No sheep peered through the back window and it was completely unlike quaint old vets' cars from TV series. Hetty was no quaint old vet, anyway. She was very much the sort of lady I like, and times are when I'd rather have my sort of lady than any sort of man.

"Hi!" She hopped out, bringing a neat black case. Her feet were elegantly heeled in delicate high sandals, but I could see wellies in the back. She wore linen trousers and a French cotton shirt. Her hair was short and fair and curled round her ears. We walked into the house together and talked about Willy.

Toby stayed very close. Like a lot of over-large dogs, he wore an air of desperate shame about his size. He hung his head, stomped slowly and drooped his ears and tail. He might, of course, have been homesick. He certainly nursed a secret sorrow. I patted the wide, bony head, and kept a hand fondling his ears. He reminded me of a school-friend called Paula (Telegraph Paula we called her) who was five foot eleven at sixteen.

"Do you think there's anything wrong?" I asked Hetty, looking at Toby with anxiety. Most of the dogs settled. Curiosity is a great comforter. Hetty ran her hand through his crisp coat the wrong way.

"Fleas," she said casually.

I jumped as if one had just bitten me. "*Fleas*!!?" and then, "Oh, *no* . . . Not fleas?" She shrugged. "Look for yourself." Her hand stayed where it was, holding back the short hairs. I could see them leaping about like Russian gymnasts.

"My God!" I cried, as if she revealed a ransom note for the christening spoon, "he's going to spread them all round the rest!"

"If he hasn't already, and not forgetting your eiderdown," agreed Hetty. She was almost enjoying it. I must say I went off her a bit.

But she reached out and patted my hand. "I'll do something about it for you." Nothing less than voodoo would satisfy me. "Flea powder and some anti-pest collars. Won't cost you more than a pound a head to keep clear. Bad cases, heavily infested, should have an Alugan bath. It's a reliable insecticide for all the mites and lice they're bound to have." She saw the look on my face. "Boarding isn't all cuddles at bedtime."

"*Mice and lites?*" I cried. I was, naturally, a bit confused. Fleas were bad enough . . .

"Infestations and parasites are merely other forms of life," protested Hetty practically. "I don't know why everyone gets the staggers about them, the way they do. OK, they're not a ball of fun and you do get more pleasure watching goldfish but they have a life too, you know, and some right to it." She made me feel a sadistic meanie. "Proletarian prejudicial snobbery!" she added, comfortingly.

On the way up the stairs, she said, "Most dogs get fleas from time to time. Or mites of some kind. It's a natural hazard for any dog leading a normal life. It's the ones who get kept indoors, away from fields and woods and freedom, that never have any. When I hear someone claim 'my dog never had a flea in his life' I feel sorry for the poor thing, nothing else. It probably spends all day in the kitchen, or in the High Street tied up outside a supermarket."

I opened the bedroom door and she went in ahead of me. "After all, dear, they might have been spiders instead of fleas." If they had been, I'd have swum half way across the Channel by now. At least, I thought, somewhat comforted, I was equal to any leaping gymnast.

The Patient was standing on the sidelines barking at Teddy, and Teddy was chasing Bustle in and out of the wardrobe. Bustle, for her part, was loving it. Her tail curled from side to side and she kept glancing roguishly over her shoulder.

Hetty stood and looked at them all. Her eyebrows rose gradually into her curly fringe. I felt embarrassed. After all, if you call in a vet for an emergency, you hardly expect the patient to be refereeing an amorous lollop over four pairs of shoes and a felt hat.

I said apologetically, "Oh, Lor' – Bustle really is a bit of a flirt. And Willy did honestly go limp and foam earlier this morning: she looked like a pair of socks up to the heel in detergent."

Hetty walked over and picked up Bustle without a word. Then she said, "It's this one who needs help. She's in season. I hope it's not too late to save us from a basket of bastards."

Strong stuff, this, I thought. Remembering Bella, I blenched. OK for some of us to chassis off down to the south of France to enjoy herself with a friend, but quite another thing when it's the kitchen bitch doing it! Upstairs/downstairs. . . ? It was so unfair – on me as well. "She never said," I wailed, "and I never thought . . ."

"It's probably early days yet," soothed Hetty, "or you'd have had an orgy under your eiderdown by now. I'll give you some pills." God knows I needed them, but she was referring to Bustle. "Make sure she takes them twice a day." And she added, "Or . . ."

The tone of her voice was warning enough. Now I knew the cause for all that scuffling the day before. They'd been getting a lot further upstairs than I had with Ross in the kitchen and I should have guessed. How naive can one get?

"My God!" I cried again, snatching Bustle into my arms. "I'll feed her nothing but, I swear. She shall dwell in isolation on a celibate bed and a diet of prophylactics." Bustle took exception to the tone of our discussion and suddenly hurled herself back on the floor again. I shut her very firmly in the cupboard. Hetty gave Willy the once-over. I asked anxiously, "Is there much wrong there?"

"Well, it's not like measles. I mean, you can't tell from a glance. But we'll give her sedatives while she's here to keep her from getting too excited." We'd all need some of those, I thought grimly. Getting to be a proper little Fun Palace, this was. Who said it was all happening elsewhere?

"Like me to look at the rest while I'm here?" Hetty suggested. She was looking at the view over the balcony with admiration. She could hardly be expected to admire the bedroom. It looked as though a bevy of burglars had been turning it over. Teddy was doing a quick act of penance in the corner.

"Kind of you but no thanks," I said hastily. "I can only take just so many problems at a time." A couple of weeks, I was thinking, and this lot would be gone. In the meantime, so long as they seemed well and happy, I wouldn't tempt providence. Hetty might find not only problems but side effects, and side effects to problems are just more problems.

I left Bustle upstairs on the bed and took Willy down. Bustle seemed content to rest after the hurly-burly of the boot rack. I made coffee and Hetty looked round and said wasn't Lady a bit on the tubby side? and Mattie's nose was warm. Treacle, she announced, had a lump on her rump. I said the lump was a bite or sting. She said it was a cyst. Something from the grass, I added firmly, and Mattie had had her nose near the boiler. Hetty said we'd have to watch it: and we glared at one another. She *almost* accused me of not caring and I *almost* accused her of touting for business.

Then we suddenly changed the subject and began talking about husbands. This made me feel guilty again, the way I do when I see a traffic warden even when my car's at home in the garage. But Hetty was the first person I'd really been able to talk to for weeks. I'd spoken to others, of course, but that's different from talking to. In spite of some opposing attitudes and occasional suspicions, Hetty and I were natural friends, the sort you can't escape, like some lovers. Close relationships between certain people are as unavoidable as thunderstorms and suffer the same sort of chemistry. So I told her about the hospital sister's call.

"I know I *ought* to go," I said, "and that I ought to *want* to go, and I think I do but how can I? I'm not doing all this for fun." I glanced round at the dogs. "Well, what with fits and cysts and warm noses, flea-sprays and anti-mating, it can't all be for kicks, can it? And it's not just pin-money or pin-ups either – you only have to see the driver of the Pets' Pantry van to know I don't get a delivery of other services along with the lungs and lites – and I don't really fancy Mr Treddie . . ." I didn't mention Ross Washington.

Hetty and I went past the porch where the dead fir tree drooped sympathetically in the broken tub. It constantly reminded me of things better forgotten, like failure and disappointment, outstanding Rates and long-standing commitments. Toby mooched behind me. He made little whimpering noises and his eyes were wide with anguish. "I really can't stand his continual suffering. He doesn't give me a chance to prove it's all going to be all right till R. Shane comes back." I felt rejected. Toby's grizzled head reminded me of a man I once knew who had a beard like that and eyes as haunting. All *his* yearning amounted to was a bottle of Scotch.

I brought Rover with me to get a bit of fresh air. Hetty was peering inside his ears, looking for trouble. She had already remarked on his lethargy with disapproval. She added, "At least he's clear of his usual trouble, canker. That's one thing you'll have to watch though."

I said, surprised, "You know him?" Someone had quietly vomited by the garden seat. I led my little party firmly beyond.

"He's a patient of mine. The Colonel's a real old love. Dotes on Rover, really dotes. I'm amazed he's gone and left him behind. He wouldn't even leave him with me when I took out his gall-bladder." I suppose she meant Rover's. He did look as if he'd lost a few parts.

"Wittering," I said. Mattie was eating someone unsavoury from the field. When she sulked, she always went off and foraged for something to make her sick. It gained sympathy and attention. Mattie was a hypochondriac: any sort of fuss was better than none.

She could lose her voice, develop a limp, get palpitations, run a rash all over, just at the drop of a rat. It didn't worry me: a few comforting words and she would make a lightning recovery, but I did get bothered about the scraps of decomposing vole, mole or mouse she was always depositing where I sat, either regurgitated or as it comes. With eyes averted, I removed half a rabbit's head from her reluctant jaws. I wondered where my earlier euphoria had gone.

"What-ing?" asked Hetty, testing Rover's teeth for trouble.

"Where do I put a thing like this before I've got a boiler going?" I dangled the head at arm's length. "Wittering. I don't know how you witter but the Colonel's doing a rush job on it. Do I wrap it and put it in the bin?" Did dustmen still scavenge for trophies?

"His wife's there, I think," said Hetty thoughtfully. "Behind the hedge."

I hurled it over, knowing it would come back eventually, but by then I might have thought of something else to do with it. Delaying tactics.

"Rover was devoted to her – more so than the Colonel, I think. He's been failing ever since she went away."

Mattie was already sniffing behind the hedge and I was completely confused. Was the dog more devoted to the Colonel's lady than the Colonel? and why had she gone away? and which of the remainder was failing the faster? My attention was a bit divided because Rosie now had the rabbit's head and was leading a noisy chase, followed closely by Teddy, Mattie and Treacle.

So I said, "I'm not quite with you . . ."

"The Colonel's wife," explained Hetty with exaggerated patience, "is in a nursing home at Wittering: it's for elderly senile patients. I doubt whether she'll ever come out now."

I forgot the rabbit's head. "Poor old man," I murmured. Then, remembering Rover, I added, "Oh, God! he'll be all right while he's here, won't he?"

"He's very old. On his last legs, I suppose you could say." I wished she wouldn't. "His heart just about ticks over, like a fading battery. Depends how long he's here . . ."

She was creating alarm and despondency. I felt frozen with dismay. Luckily Maribou strolled round the corner dragging a quite disgusting rabbit skin. It must have been around for months. Mrs Flutey would have fainted.

Hetty said, "You don't have a Baby Bunting by any chance?" and at the same moment I muttered, "We only need the tail to have a set" – and the tension was eased.

When we got back to the kitchen, Rover lay in his box panting, eyes closed. His jowls hung loose, showing a few yellowish teeth and a pale lining to the slack mouth. Even Frilly seemed uneasy.

"He is all right?" I pleaded.

Hetty knelt down and picked up a paw. Then she let it go. It fell limp. "Well, no," she said reluctantly. "I don't think he is." She was pulling down his eye, feeling his pulse – checking he wasn't dead, for God's sake! I was terrified. No dog had ever died on me: well, not just like that. Times were when I stayed while the necessary mercy injection was given, and watched the faithful old life ebb away, cried my way home, repeating the already fading name and leaving behind a love and memory that few men could equal. But this . . .

"He won't? Not here? I couldn't bear it! How would I tell the old man? Hetty, for God's sake!" She gave me a long, cool look and got up. I felt sudden shame.

"Did he bring the pills I gave him?" I nodded.

"Has he been having them regularly?" I nodded again.

"Then he should be OK. Let's give him one now." I handed her the pill-ball searching recollections of daily dosing to comfort myself. It had seemed enough just to have a neat shelf where First Aid was on hand for cuts and things, and where ear drops and eye drops revealed an effort at efficiency even if I was failing the acid test at that very minute. And for that daunting moment, it was for me the bruised lilies, the surplus herbs, the late tomatoes and the gentleman's dung all over again.

Then Hetty said gently, "My dear, it's no good falling at the first fence. He's going to be all right for a while yet and the Colonel won't be at Wittering any longer than he can help. Let's face it, if the old thing does die, you can comfort yourself that you took the agony of the end from the old man's shoulders. He may think he would have been able to keep the dog alive longer: he may blame himself for going away. He may even blame you – but does that matter so much if you relieved him of those harrowing final hours?"

At last it was all in perspective. Life and death are both too big to be dodged, and when they hit you it's essential to keep your balance. How I felt hardly mattered at all any more.

I gave Hetty a look of gratitude. Then I knelt down by the box and smoothed away the last shreds of panic with my fingers.

Hetty said, "I'll have to go. I really must. I've got to castrate a horse."

I got up and saw her to the door. It was hard to imagine anyone so like the cover girls on *Cosmopolitan* doing anything so basic. I said so.

"It was a pig yesterday." I did wonder what else would be in the next collection of heads and trotters.

She paused. "You're still trembling."

Tears filled my eyes. I said, "I'm a bit tired, I suppose." It was an under-statement.

"Look," said Hetty firmly, "if I can make a quick phone call, we could have a drink to Rover before I go. We'll sit down outside under the trees again and you'll relax if I have to knock you out to do it. Go on, get something with some alcohol in it. How about a Dachsund's Nose – long and cold?"

I made it grapefruit, ice and a good dash of gin. I still use the same formula when relaxing after moments of stress. And there's always plenty of those around. When I went back to the seat under the tree, Hetty had her feet up on the round Britannia table and her eyes were closed against the sun.

"It's OK, the horse is going to wait. I was out half the night with an old boar."

"We've all made that mistake," I said, attempting a joke.

We clinked glasses.

"I see I'll have to sort you out," Hetty said. "I mean it." Her feet swung down and she stopped me from protesting. "Do let me. I'm good at it. Some time you can have a go at doing the same thing for me when I need it." I couldn't imagine such a time being any more likely than my being asked to board a royal corgi.

The dogs had gone in. Sun never tempted them as it did me. I wondered if we were all too sensitive to weather. Give Rosie a Force 9 gale or a howling storm and she'd be out and away, shaking back the long untidy hair like a teenager at a disco date, whooping it up round the burrows. But a warm sunny morning often had her creeping back into the house to lie on the cold hall floor.

"As I see it, then," went on Hetty, a bit pompously, "you rushed into a project with more haste than how-to. OK, so the idea was fine. It may have been just a trifle haphazard though?"

"Not the way *I* saw it when I put the ad. in the paper." Anyway, it still seemed all right. Those nice kennels, time to spare, family holidays about to begin . . . It wasn't even like the parsley which I thought would flourish into neat little plastic drums, or the lilies, wafting direct to burial grounds. Though I must admit it's the work in the middle I sometimes get wrong.

"Some time when I have longer, we can go into it all on paper as a commercial proposition," said Hetty, sighing. Mainly in relief, I think, that we couldn't then. "But as it is, let's just cover the basics. To start with, have you made any money yet?" It was, for me, a sore thumb, but I did have some very able fingers in the pie. I shrugged.

"Then it's a case of tiding over till you can afford a publicity campaign and staff." She made it all sound so terribly grand.

"To begin with," she went on, "I'll be in most mornings to look at Rover. He's my patient and I think I ought to. No, it's OK. I have to pass on my way to Feathers Farm. They've got a herd of pregnant goats. Billies have to be put down early, but I'll get you a nanny and kid when I can. There's your milk bill paid and plenty over for the dogs. Fred Feather might agree to a barter basis . . ."

"What on earth do I have to barter?" I said wildly, seeing myself part with the final shreds of home for some repulsive antlered she-goat. Better to go on the milk wagon altogether than drag a shower of lactating nannies into the parlour.

"Eggs," said Hetty, looking smug.

"Ah! but I don't have any hens," I countered, even smugger.

"Not yet, you don't." We looked at one another warily.

"Not *ever*, I don't," I warned her, very very firmly. I had kept hens before.

Hetty said we'd probably see, wouldn't we? Then she said I wasn't to fret about old Rover. "He'll wait for his master to come home before he does anything as important as dying. My old sealy-ham bitch, Mouldy, would never have her puppies until I was there. She once waited until the end of a holiday in Switzerland. She was four days overdue. She practically burst as I walked in the door, and had five puppies on the Axminster before I could take off my skis!"

She got in her little car. "The other dogs'll do, and I shall recommend you everywhere. There's a shortage of really good kennelling round here. You should have a full house in no time. Once you're house-tied and coping with six you may as well be coping with sixty. Think of the money –" she saw my mounting dismay "– and you could move into the kennels yourself! I'll drop in with all the pills and sprays and things later today. Now, do remember to ask for relevant dates when you book in bitches. And if they can't give you any, disclaim all responsibility. Better have that printed on the forms" (what forms?) "and watch closely." She started the engine and shouted, "No good merely *isolating* bitches . . ." and the car slid away. On the breeze, her voice rang out warningly, "You must use spray *and* tablets or you'll have a howling mob on a gang-bang!"

I looked round uneasily, but no one was listening except Toby, and his embarrassment was greater than mine.

Those long, easy days spent beneath the trees with a book, watching the frisky gambols of my little four-legged friends over the meadows, vanished down a sordid spout of lechery and medication.

Just as I turned to go in, the little car reversed back up the drive at great speed and came to a stop with a skid that shot the gravel all over the borders. Hetty shouted, "As for your husband, look at it this way. He's better. That's what matters. Now be firm about what you can, and cannot, do. Ring him up but *don't* say how devastated you are you can't come and hold his hand on his trip to the coast. Simply say how lucky he is to be going. Say you wish you could be promised a holiday, too. Be positive. Make sure you get in a few of your problems. But be cheerful with it. Go on about it being simply a sticky patch you have to battle through alone with your usual Courage and Forbearance. Don't whine though. Carry the war into his own camp, flags flying, and make *him* feel guilty for a change. Keep on repeating, 'Now, you're not to worry about me. I'll be all right.' There's nothing more guaranteed to hint at despair."

She switched off the engine and warmed to the subject.

"You can add, 'I was able to get four or five hours' sleep last night' – drop in one or two things about how much you'll save doing the decorating yourself. You don't have to say you're actually doing it. Look, you must have been married longer than me, you must know how it goes, surely?" She sounded impatient. "It's only kind, after all. To him, I mean. If he's aware of your problems here, his own will diminish in contrast. Now, don't apologise even once. Say you wish you could be there as it would mean *a whole day off* for you. He must be convinced he's got the best end of the wishbone. Got it?"

The second time she shot away, I thought she looked a bit like a manipulating Siamese cat. I didn't like her any the less, but she did make me feel the humble tabby. If she could continue to look, and stay, feminine and gorgeous in the work she was doing, there was no reason at all why I should deteriorate into one of those shapeless ladies in sack aprons who almost always get associated with livestock of one kind or another.

I went back to the kitchen and peered in the mirror by the door. I would pluck my eyebrows next time I got a bath. A bath? I rang the fuel suppliers and ordered coke and coal and anthracite with the abandon of Satan expecting company.

The pigs' heads were due out of the Aga: a pan of trotters and other less nameable parts were ready. I made myself look at them, take a knife and begin to cut them up. There was no more to it than carving the Sunday joint. Less, perhaps. At least I was doing it all for others. Nevertheless, I had a nasty suspicion it would ruin every hotel breakfast I ordered for the rest of my life.

Something really had happened. Maybe I was catching some of Hetty's tough approach. Call it self-survival: yesterday I served the dinners with head averted (slicing bits off my fingers) but today I might have been dishing up ice cream. It made things a great deal easier. My mind ran on into printed forms, organised walks, regulated everything. I moved about briskly, using Sister Maude's tone to Rover, summoning the rest of the dogs to their meal from places where they were lounging about like weekend guests avoiding the washing-up.

And when they'd finished, I hooked them all to their leads and led them first for a quick walk round the drive and woods, then back to the kennels where I distributed them firmly, one in each. I took a large watering-can and filled the water bowls. Then I said, "It's not for long. Just an hour or so to give myself something I need more than you do. A bit of freedom and a rest." And I walked in, a blind eye to the afghans' dismay, Toby's pink pads against the wire netting, Willy's funny little lost bark and, eventually as I rushed into the kitchen, Bustle's pathetic howl.

"Oh God!" I said aloud to Rover, the sole remaining boarder in the house, "it's not that bad! They'll even grow to like it after a while." Then I got out the chalk and wrote "POSITIVE ACTION WILL BRING RELIEF".

It sounded like a commercial for senna pods.

9

I let them out fifteen minutes later.

It wasn't so much the yaps and howls and barks that bugged me. It was because I couldn't stand the house without them in it.

We all trooped back into the kitchen. Solemnly I handed round ginger snaps and switched on Radio 2 again. Whatever happened, disc jockeys restore some sense of balance, however banal. Mentalities settle down to their level, emotions are suffused into a cosy fog, and we push the valium back in the bottle.

Hetty had brought me the loaves and sausages. I could get butter from the milkman who already left the eggs. I glanced at the brown paper so recently pinned on the wall by the dresser and made up my newly positive mind to cut out the worry of shopping altogether. For the rest of the season I would stay where I was and let the shopping come to me. What couldn't come, could stay where it was. The decision was a flash of true inspiration and would relieve me of one worry at least.

I rang the village shop.

"Good afternoon, Miss Priddle," I said rather grandly. I gave my name and address to remind her of our earlier meeting. Then I said, "I am about to give an order." It sounded exactly like Napoleon addressing his troops, so I hurried on. "Can you get me such things as paint? Cheap? Wholesale, perhaps? I'm tied to the house by my responsibilities," and *that* sounded like corset-strings, "so I can't even come down and see you. I shall have to ask you to bring everything if you possibly can!" I waited. But she did too, so I added, "I need plastic buckets and bowls, shampoos, scrubbing brushes, paint brushes, account books, mascara and gin."

I paused again, but you couldn't throw a lady like that except in a judo ring. She said calmly, "Four bottles or a case?" and we both laughed.

I said I'd make a list and ring her again. I felt terrific. Very affirmative. I went back and spoke to Rover with such encouragement and confidence, he caught on to the moment and put up his old head, wagged his tail so that it thumped the sides of his box, and alerted his ears. I began to believe I could run the whole business on positive thinking. I would save Rover, the situation and my own sanity.

There were deep drawers in the dresser. I cleared one of the odds and ends dumped there by the removal men and neatly arranged my diary, exercise books labelled Appointments and Bookings, two pens and a notebook for temporary accounting. I chalked, "LET NOTHING DISTURB THEE, NOTHING AFFRIGHT THEE, EVERYTHING PASSES" and found a space for it to the right of the fridge. Then I took the scissors I use for cutting bacon rind, and trimmed my hair. There was an air of purpose everywhere, as if the house waited for my next trick.

I decided it would be a room prepared to receive clients. So far, they'd drifted in and out of the kitchen, nimbly avoiding dogs underfoot. I chose the small breakfast room because it was warm – lots of sun and the back of the kitchen boiler along one wall. The wallpaper was a faded William Morris. Patches where pictures had been taken down were easily covered by my own. I chose a collection of Thornton flower prints. The dogs were suitably impressed. They watched, followed me about, sparred together under my feet, and tried out the chairs. I talked to them all the time. After an hour or two the room, cleaned, polished and rearranged, was a phoenix of positive thought risen from the ashes of indecision.

I made a cheese sandwich to keep me going, put some sausages covered with the remains of a bottle of cider in the slow oven and rang the hospital. Hetty's abrasive advice had to be put into operation before it wore off.

But the time they took to put me through did a lot to ebb the tide of courage.

"Hullo," I said briskly, when I heard Pa pick up the phone. "How are you?"

"I'm not too good this evening." He was ahead of me.

I came in quickly with, "Excitement, I expect. You're off soon, they tell me?"

"Tomorrow. What time are you going to be here?"

"I should be so lucky," I chuckled bitterly. "Still, never mind. I did get nearly five hours' sleep last night. Mustn't grumble!"

"Where the hell had you been?" he demanded, taking the wind out of my sails.

I replied stiffly, "Working – stoking boilers, cleaning paintwork, laying carpets, hanging curtains . . ."

He interrupted. "All right, all right. Bring my thin dressing-gown and at least two sweaters. It may be windy down there. Oh yes, and a new pyjama cord and some wellies. You'd better bring a few things yourself. You'll have to stay overnight. They're short of staff, too, and I don't want some wretched trainee getting me settled. You know what they get in during the summer? *Students*! I'm not having that. I'm not having bloody amateurs making my bed . . ." You'd have thought he was talking about terrorists.

"I'm sure they're very nice students. I don't know why you're in such a state. I'll send on everything right away. You should get them in a couple of days. I'll ring tomorrow evening, of course, see how it went, what the place is like, all that. They tell me these young students are often very pretty girls with sympathetic ambitions to help . . ."

But he wasn't to be side-tracked. "You don't mean you're not coming?"

"Of course, I do. I can't possibly, you know that. I do so wish I could. I need a day off. My God, I'd *love* to see the sea, eat a meal I haven't cooked, watch television again . . ." The ring of anguish was enough to stop a steamroller, but it did nothing for this one.

"You mean to say you think more of the housework than you do of me? Well, that's a change, I must say! It can all wait, surely?"

"But the *dogs* can't" I wailed, aware my approach was faulty somewhere." I do have a number of boarders here now, but you mustn't worry about me! I'll manage it all somehow, just as long as I can keep going."

"So it's the dogs, is it? Doesn't matter about how I feel!"

In that precise moment he was dead right. "Look," I said, "do try and be reasonable. How else are we to manage? I'm trying to organise a business and I'm not doing it for the sheer hell of a good time."

"OK OK," he said wearily, "It's all my fault. I should have been a dog!" I almost agreed. "Anyway," he went on cheerfully, taking over the role of martyr, "it hardly matters about me, at my age!" and he put the phone down.

I was incensed. To start with, I hate any reference to age as a reason, excuse, plea or demand. No one is any different a person from conception to final collection. I was quite sharp with Mrs Flutey when she rang a few moments later.

"All well? No problems? Motions regular? Firm? Good. OK for 14th? Say 2.30? Remember anal trim! File claws Fridays. Right?"

I said, "Sure thing. OK. All well. Goodbye," and put the phone down too.

It rang again at once. My husband said, in a contrite, little-lad-with-broken-hoop voice, "I'm *so* sorry, darling. I was a right bastard, wasn't I? Of course I understand. I'm just being bloody-minded, as always."

Remorse is as potent as Glauber Salts, and I dissolved the same way.

"It's all my fault," I wailed, putting Hetty's advice firmly from my mind. "Letting you down when you needed me. I'm such a lousy manager. I couldn't organise a game of Snap!" And I realised we were both playing the other's hand, especially when he finished:

"Now just you stop worrying about me. I'll get by. Bad penny, you know! You were right about the students. My special one looks like Angharad Rees, never saw such hair, and hands as soft and gentle as a kitten's . . ." I looked at Frilly, busy ripping the stuffing out of a chair arm. But he was going on, "And you're marvellous! You could manage anything, cope with a dozen disasters. You're so capable, so practical really." It made me sound like a female storm-trooper compared to little fluffy Angharad Nightingale. He ended anxiously, ". . . now you won't forget the pyjama-cord, will you?"

I didn't think he was planning to hang himself but if so, the request would have ranked with any of the other famous Last Words in history. I went upstairs, there and then, and found two. They might, I thought furiously, just like to go together . . .

IO

Before going to bed that night, I took the dogs out in two groups. Because they had no territorial rights of their own to defend, none of them objected to the presence of the rest and, apart from occasional mild complaints and disagreements, they all got along very well. My own three accepted whatever I appeared to consider right and proper. They were happily confident, and prepared to share if requested. Anyway, Rosie was almost as gregarious as I would have been: Treacle had a pronounced streak of maternal responsibility, and only Mattie disassociated herself at all. We were like a rather jolly progressive school, peace-loving and aiming at nothing more ambitious than integrated communal living.

It was very dark outside. A mean moon spared very little light, and down on the Motorway the strange, almost eerie glow of night-glares hung misty and thick. The afghans stood aloof from the rest, like members of a Gay Lib Group who had wandered into the Rugby Club by mistake. Toby kept close behind me, his sad noble nose mere inches from my uneasy shoulder and ear. My own three ran loose, the envy of the rest on leads. Even though the walls built round the whole small estate made it fairly secure, I felt distinctly unwilling to spend half the night rounding up reckless wanderers.

Rover was extremely particular about going out at regular intervals. His inside was as well-drilled as an army platoon. I took him on his own and even if he had been hyper-sensitive instead of the way he was, a lead would have been unnecessary. Rover would have acted responsibly on all occasions.

There was just time to wash my hair before bed including dipping it in cold tea, tidy up a bit, refill the Aga ovens with pigs' heads, and try to catch up with the News on the radio. But the world's problems sounded small fry compared to mine. And so, of course, did their few joys and triumphs.

Bustle, pilled and sprayed, had retired to her blanket. Her coat had been brushed and combed. So had Willy's and Teddy's. The afghans I groomed every morning. Frilly was tucked in with Rover. I locked up, turned out the lights, and started up the wide oak staircase with Toby on my heels. It was about halfway that he stopped suddenly and gave a short sharp bark. Then he turned and hurtled himself down the stairs again. He was quivering with excitement at the back door when I caught up with him, his nose to the crack underneath, whimpering and panting.

I was really scared. It was obvious he must have heard something, but then, I tried to tell myself, he was always waiting for disaster, like a maiden aunt at the Tarot cards. "Toby, come on, bedtime, quickly!" but he ignored me completely. Who, or what, was outside? A fox? an owl? even the wind getting up? But these things had never troubled him before. I went to the door, grasped his collar firmly and shouted loud enough for anyone out there to hear, "It's all right, darling, I'll go! Tell Harry and Joe to come on down and get some judo practice!" But my voice quavered and the last few words were nervous squeaks. Then, wisely or unwisely, I slipped the chain enough to open the door a crack and peer through.

Toby was shivering and crying. His tail told me something good was out there. Something which didn't threaten our safety. His nose worked overtime, his whiskers bristled. He was trying to get outside, but I held on tightly. I leant away, switched on the porch light and peered out.

Then, with its tiny nose meeting the snuffling muzzle, its upright tail flipping and flirting, and with little cries from them both, Tobias and the Angel were reunited. She was obviously of Siamese extraction, but with a strong dash of tortoiseshell to patch her small, pansy face. The prettiest kitten I think I ever saw.

"Hull*oo*!" I said. "And where on earth have you been?"

There was no doubt at all about who she was. She must have been hiding in the barns. Toby's owner would have left them together, trusting to mutual devotion to keep it that way. I felt a surge of anger at whoever he was, this R. Shane. I thought of the anguish in Toby's eyes since I found him, and saw the kitten's ribs through its smooth furry sides, and I looked forward to R. Shane coming back when I could pound him to pulp with words to show the way I felt.

The kitten slipped inside and I chained the door again, watching Toby with delight. He was suddenly a different dog, bounding, leaping, excited. I reached down and picked up the tiny little thing and hugged it.

Frilly sat up and stared. Slowly and ostentatiously she saw fit to wash a taut leg, her eyes on the Angel while it downed a saucer of creamy milk and some of Frilly's own favourite catfood. Then she leapt nimbly out of Rover's box and strolled across. They were much the same age, but the Angel had Toby on her side. Frilly stalked stiff-legged back to the box. Rover was on hers.

I watched Toby washing the kitten with great rough smacks of his huge tongue while it reached out and grabbed at his ears and nose with small prickly paws. Then I left them in the breakfast room with Toby's blanket on the sofa and thankfully went up to bed.

During the night, Bustle fell on Maribou as she turned over, and caused a mild disturbance because Maribou jumped and clutched Willy. They all settled back with sighs and were asleep again before I was, but I lay there comforted by the small warm bodies close to mine, and the security they gave me. Their trust in me, love and confidence were mystical magic in a world of harsh realities. I finally fell asleep myself, utterly content.

Came the dawn and I found Willy's paw had reached out during the night and was resting gently in my face cream. Still asleep, she was covered in Overnight Sensitised Moisturising Emollient. At £2.00 a jar I must have been mad to think it would be worth a try. Even madder to leave the lid off. It was probably perfumed lard anyway. I wrapped the greasy paw in tissues and slipped an old sock over the top finished with a ribbon bow to keep it in place. I hoped it would do more for Willy's paw than it had ever done for my face.

Nobody got up when I did that day. There's nothing a dog can do at six in the morning if he can't hang wallpaper. In the kitchen, Rover quivered slightly in his sleep, but his nose was cool and damp. Small mercies were all I could hope for. Toby slept with a smile on his huge face and the kitten tucked under his chin. I felt tears well up as I realised why the dog had been so tormented with worry since he had been left. He must have felt he was failing his master and his beloved companion. I should have realised it was more than heart-ache from homesickness.

I put on the kettle and answered the phone with the other hand. At that hour I hoped it wasn't the hospital with some ultimatum. I'd already packed the pyjama cords and the enormous parcel was ready for Humphrey to collect. Armed with protests and self-defence, I said "Hullo?" more warily than revealingly.

It was Marsha. "Darling. How are you? I'm on my way up to you – well, after I've been to bed a few hours. Just got in." She didn't say from what or where, and I didn't ask. I was too horrified.

"Up *here*?" I asked, most ungraciously.

"Yes, darling, and I'm bringing Timmy and Bongo."

Timmy, the witch's familiar, her tabby cat, I knew only too well. He was a sinister character from which even the most dominant fell back.

"Who on earth is Bongo?"

"You'll adore him, darling. He's been staying a day or two." All the friends Marsha fleetingly made were, according to her, adorable, until they walked out with her handbag, made off with her mink or sidled away with her sister taking Marsha's car at the same time.

"Look, Marsha," I said firmly, "you can't. I have absolutely nothing here except dogs and offal. The house is falling apart. I shall have no hot water until they send some coke. It's very primitive. Quite horrible. And no beds, either, except mine and that's overcrowded."

"Rubbish," said Marsha briskly, then yawning. "You still have a few chairs, I presume? I can sleep anywhere." Her voice thickened. She was almost asleep on the phone. "The weather's too good for city life. Besides, Bongo is really longing to leave London. He's not used to being here at all. I'll bring some microbiotic goodies." Marsha never ate anything which wasn't packaged in a health shop, though we both knew for certain, if with tacit agreement to ignore it, that quite a lot of it was precisely what she could have bought in any supermarket, with different labelling but for half the price.

"Who is Bongo?" I asked. I was always steam-rollered by Marsha. Her three marriages and innumerable gurus and lovers (I never knew one from another) had given her a force which was unable to take into account any other outside opposition. She just knew that anything she wanted to do was right for us all. It was the only real asset she acquired from any of the cults and religions she took up and dropped with the frequency of her own underwear.

"He's a love," she purred, "Tibetan. Steeped in philosophy. He'll eat very little. Drinks spring water and he'll bring his own nuts."

I tried brutal honesty. "I don't want anyone here at all, not even you and, er, Bongo. Not until I'm a bit more organised and a lot less busy."

"That's just why we're on our way," she said. "To help." She added, "Bongo – it's not his real name, darling, just one I gave him. His own is most terribly awkward, a sort of embroidered obscenity – Bongo might even stay on a few weeks. Unluckily, I have to go back before the end of the month because of Sven." I didn't ask about Sven. I was too angry about Bongo.

There was a woman peering at me through the small window in the porch. I said, "Why don't you have a long sleep and ring me when you wake? I'll give you directions about finding us then," and remembered gratefully that so far she only had my telephone number.

The woman at the door was like a beer barrel in floral silk. There seemed to be leaks in the barrel because she was damp everywhere it showed. Under one arm she carried a scowling pekinese. Anyone would have scowled under there.

"I *am* so sorry to just pop in this way," she apologised, panting in perfect unison with the peke, "but the vet gave me your address and your number doesn't seem to be in The Book." She made it sound like holy writ. To some, Yellow Pages is little less. "So I had to just arrive." She laughed, but the effort left her limp.

"Come in and sit down a minute," I said sympathetically, holding out my arms for the grumpy peke. She passed it over and I gave at the knees. It weighed half as much as its mistress and that was about as much as anyone could take.

She sank down on a chair, sighing. "That's the worst of winter," she explained irrelevantly.

"What is?" I was puzzled because outside the sun was growing hotter by the minute.

"Oh, you know. Eating, no exercise . . ." She laughed grimly. "Putting on extra weight with Christmas and that."

"Yes," I said, "yes, of course" though it was nearly six months since that season of self-indulgence. Maybe she hadn't observed the rigours of Lent.

"Now I'm off to a health farm for a week, and I hope you'll mind my baby for me." For an instant I was startled. But she was beaming at the peke. She went on, "He can't come with me. I did ask. I said he needed a little off here and there too, but no, they said they were not an animal health farm."

An annexe! I would open An Annexe. For dieting dogs! Then I remembered how much they looked forward to their dinners, and I forgot it as a Feature of the Establishment in my Future Prospectus.

"And so," she finished, "Mrs. Hebditch said we should come here."

"Only to board of course," I concluded for her.

"She did say you were marvellous with animals and you would probably help him lose a little round his tum." I looked at the peke. The bulging eyes, panting tongue and the way he sat awkwardly spreading the load, like anyone's elderly aunt, was an appeal in itself.

I said uneasily, "I'll see what I can do. Can't promise much, but, well, we'll try and limit his luxuries." I knew he must wallow in chocolate mousse and cream cakes. And it was easy enough to assure her he wouldn't get that sort of thing with us.

She said her name was Mrs Roland Frobisher of Roland Frobisher Antiques. The dog was called Mr Pekin Pearl but they called him Perky at home. He was anything but that. I said I thought Percy suited him better (although I would have spelled it Pursey – I never saw a more opulent dog) and she smiled vaguely and said he didn't come when he was called because he found it hard to hear through all that coat. She was quite proud of the fact. I waited till she was gone and then had a look inside both ears and found them stuffed up with hair and wax. Once we'd got all that away, I had a reckless clip round his eyes with the blunt-ended scissors so he could see better, and to clear away the hairs that might get on to the actual eye and cause ulcers. He sat like a lump of lard and let me have my way with him and made not the slightest protest. I don't really think he noticed. He was lost in a world of surplus fat, but somewhere a nice little dog was dying to get out.

Mrs Roland Frobisher had left an envelope together with his brush and comb and ribbons and cushion and blanket and so on. Inside, she said, were instructions about his "routine". I thought she meant his weight and nodded sagely, expecting to find advice about leaving off all carbohydrates and a good few calories as well. Instead there was a £5 note with a slip of paper attached. It read "Perky's pocket-money". I presumed it was for Mars Bars and double cream.

Humphrey had taken the parcel. I had to get Marsha off my mind, not to mention the dreaded Bongo. But it was almost impossible to think up something to put her right off. Meantime I decided it would be prudent to ring the hospital.

Sister Maude came to the phone with such alacrity I knew something was simmering to be said. It had always been so difficult to get through to her. I don't think, looking back, I ever really did get through to her.

"Good morning, Sister. How is my husband today?"

Usually she would go through all the routine of "Name, please?" and the "I must refer to my charts" bit, but now she said, with relish, summoning up all her reserves of disapproval not usually on show, "He's gone, I'm afraid."

For one appalling moment, suspended in time, I thought she meant – but then I knew she meant me to think that way, and I refused to fall for it. So I said calmly, "Oh dear, I've missed him. Never mind."

I heard her draw in her breath. Then she said sharply, "He went half an hour ago," but it failed to have the impact planned.

"Good," I said cheerfully. "Can you give me his new number please? Up there or down there or wherever they took him." I couldn't resist that.

She gave in and said grudgingly that he'd be tired after completing the journey *on his own* but I accepted that as fair comment though I longed to express surprise that they were letting him *drive* an ambulance. Instead, I asked gently whether he had been quite well before he left, and she had the chance to say, "Naturally, or we should have kept him here till he was!"

I suddenly felt a great pang of guilt, mixed with shattering sympathy for someone I well knew to be more vulnerable, emotionally, than most in spite of a defensive barrier of indifference. I wished with all my heart that it had been possible for me to go with him. But I knew Sister M wanted me to admit I was repentant so I said, instead, "I'm sure he'll be fine, you've looked after him *so* well. We both thank you for all your kindness, Sister, and for all you've done for us both. I couldn't have left him in better hands! Believe me, we really are most grateful." I meant it, too. OK, so she had been impossible to me, but I knew she felt justified. I could understand that. Even appreciate it. The attitude was taken on behalf of her patient, and no one was more grateful for that than I was.

She said stiffly, "I'm glad we could be of help."

"Well," I went on, "neither of us will ever forget you." That was true, anyway. She coughed uneasily and muttered, "I only did my duty" – which was what I had suspected all along. And a little warmth with it would have been rather nice.

It sent me quite mad with confidence and I pushed my luck over the edge. "Florence Nightingale herself could have done no more!" I declaimed in ringing tones. These days, poor old Flo N. is revealed as not all the Angel of Mercy she was once thought to be, due to certain revelations about her private life which may have been better left concealed. Sister snapped back, "I just hope he'll get on all right now he's left us," as if she doubted it very much, "and that we don't see him back here again." With that double-edged dig she added she had a lot to do and Good Day.

I felt a bit better when I put down the phone. I had the new number to ring and now I could find out how he was without steaming into battle every time. I could relax, knowing he was recuperating by the sea and in better hands than these which dismembered, sprayed, de-loused and then soothed, and smoothed. Our son was tramping somewhere over Ethiopia so far as I knew, our daughter living out my own fantasies in reality and in the most desirable place in the Western hemisphere with the most desirable man she had yet found. Another daughter was safe, married and happy with an incredible red-haired and beautiful baby. We were all in love and in touch. There was nothing in the world to worry about, unless it was the car coming up the drive – and then I saw whose car it was.

No one could get to the States and back in such a short time and yet seem to have been away six months, unless it was Ross

Washington. I turned to the mirror and tidied my hair. I used the pink lipstick I keep in my pocket, recalling my mother's advice always to appear at the door as if some past lover was going to be waiting. The afghans (who mattered even more) had been brushed and were stretched out on their wickerwork. I left them there, in the conservatory, looking like languid Edwardian ladies in a scene from "The End of the British Empire". Willy and Teddy lay outside in the sunshine like two pensioners bored on a package tour to Majorca. Toby and the Angel were teasing Frilly in the breakfast room, so relieved to be together that the embarrassing dogged faithfulness to me was forgotten, thank goodness. Bustle was in the shopping basket, Maribou was playing with one of Percy's soft toys and Percy was searching eagerly for crumbs in the carpet sweeper. Lady lay with her eye on the telephone.

It was peaceful and pleasant. It became positively euphoric when Ross stood facing the house. I didn't have to resort to a listed Smile: the beam came naturally.

I made coffee and carried the tray under the trees, followed by Bob and Bill. None of us gave anything away emotionally. From them, there had been the leisurely lift of the paw, the acknowledgement by an incline of the head, a gracious acceptance of fondled ears and some slight movements of the tail in a measured, calculated demonstration of delight. That was all until Bill had rested his long, aristocratic nose inside Ross's hand with a deep sigh, closing heavily fringed eyes and showing utter content. Now they lay one either side of him, like Staffordshire figures.

"Are you here to take them home?" I asked, wondering how much to charge. Hetty had suggested we work out charges together to cover all possible risks and costs, and I presumed this included her regular visits as well. Her own account was never mentioned. So far as the dogs were concerned, I had said why not an overall cover charge by the yard. Hetty had replied, "Why not the foot?" We never got any further.

Ross lay back and stretched out his long graceful legs. The old thing about dogs resembling owners and vice versa did have a basis in truth, I now realised. He was saying, "No. There was a message at the airport calling me back to town. I'm just off again. I thought you wouldn't mind if I called around to tell you something."

Oh, no! I thought . . . and yet, Oh, yes! I hoped, like a yearning adolescent. I smiled, unsurprised, as if men called regularly to declare their devotion.

"Give you something, really," he went on.

Oh, well – but what? Money? His mother's wedding ring? A lock of his hair? It wasn't that abundant when you looked closely from behind, I thought wildly. He pulled something out of his pocket. His hands were lean and brown: I could have done without the long white envelope if he had only suggested I take them instead.

My God, another list of instructions, I thought, groaning inwardly. I was fast developing a nasty case of the anti-list phobias. A few individual details were OK, such as praying and sneeze-stifling, but I was beginning to resent the minute interpretations every owner considered lay beneath a bark, or the detailed health routines any terminal geriatric would have considered a violation of human rights.

Ross went on, "Pedigrees, Kennel Clûb cards and a signed statement that if anything happens to me I'd like you to have the dogs. If you feel unable to accept the risk, of course I'll understand and arrange for them to be put down. I have a sense of responsibility towards them, naturally, and we only have one another now." I felt shocked. On such a day in such a place. And why me?

"Surely you don't anticipate the remote possibility . . .?" I hesitated. The man was consumed by doom unless he really *was* some sort of James Bond under-cover agent.

"You never can be sure . . ." he protested mildly.

He didn't look like a man about to jump off the end of the pier. It would be a terrible waste if he did. Had some solemn doctor in a West End consulting-room called him back at the last moment, from the airport, yesterday? Just to tell him the tests were positive and he had three months at the most? Was he, perhaps, on a mission for MI5 and knew too well there would be no tomorrow? Dying nobly to perish under a hail of bullets in some South American swamp? I stared in horror.

"Hey," he said anxiously, "don't get carried away. It's hardly a possibility. But I'm a reasonably responsible dog-owner. I like to leave everything easily settled by anyone who might have to deal with my affairs."

I still thought it a bit morbid. Why, you might as well will the cat to the postman every time you cross the road.

I asked if he was nervous of flying. It sounded a bit off as I said it because honestly I'd have backed his courage against an amble of crocodiles any time.

But he didn't mind. "Not so much nervous, as aware. And not just of flying but of cars that crash, bombs that explode and people with knives in their teeth leaping out of dark corners. And anyone who isn't, lacks something, I imagine."

He was laughing a bit, but I could see what he meant. After all you could be strangled tying your tie or choke to death over a currant bun. You had to be aware of the hurdles, not afraid of them, or you'd never get over the top.

Then he said rather an odd thing. "But this trip won't be peanuts." It could have meant anything but the way he said it had a hint of Bogart. Words like Mafia, micro-film and weed or speed flickered a moment, then went out.

The coffee was finished. He said, "How about the other four mugs?" and we smiled again, together. The silence falling between us was shared, too, not laboured. "Played any good early morning tennis lately?" I wanted a slick retort but had to make do with a short, meaningless laugh. Lauren Bacall could have done it a lot better.

We sat on, talking about places and dogs and other non-committal things. The sun was exaggerating the day. It had a strange effect. I began to feel more and more like some landowner's lady in the Deep South with nothing better to do than flirt with Clark Gable. (I never can equate contemporary acting with romances.)

Using a new line in slow smiles (No. 11) dredged up from a box of unused items in my emotional attic, I said, "Shall we have a cool drink? I thought, say, a medlar juice with ice?" It would have been nice to clap my hands for a servant, but if I tried, even in my fantasy, Rosie would doubtless arrive with a dead rabbit.

There seems to have been the same tin of medlar juice in every fridge I've ever owned. I always left it there, gradually rusting, because it looked impressive. I hoped it would be glimpsed by visitors. We rarely had any fridge-fumbling visitors but we never drank the medlar juice, just in case.

I carried the long glasses, clinking with ice, back to the garden, resisting an impulse to rush upstairs, take a quick bath, wash my hair, change into some seductive gown and sidle back, all in five minutes. But this was no commercial for a hair-fixative, so I merely kept my feet out of sight to hide my horrible toenails.

"This really is the most wonderful place," he murmured, eyes half-closed against the sun. "I shall remember it when I've gone." My heart thumped. I wished he would stop hinting about something dark and possibly fatal in the future. Was he, though, acting out the role of a dark-skinned guerrilla, snatching a final hour of passion from desperate warfare in the Bush? I may have had my facts wrong because I hardly ever go to the cinema and the television still churns out Greer Garsons on Sunday afternoons, and those vintage Sinatras where they all play at being goodies and baddies. People like me have to rely on film reviews and posters. With my first surplus in the till, I would definitely get the television re-connected and catch up. It's possible we were up to Julie Andrews by now.

I forgot the work that waited, the walls that were stripped for action, like a fan-dancer in the wings. The sun and the company, the regular breathing of two lovely dogs, and the relief from what threatened to become a fetish of problems lulled me into a delicious state of euphoria. Then the phone rang.

It had to be that or a dog choking. "Excuse me" I said, in a voice which tried to convey that I would sooner have leapt from the roof than leave his side. I snatched the phone and growled at it.

"Look," said my husband's voice without waiting a moment to see if I was ready, willing and able, "nothing's arrived. *Nothing*."

With open doors and windows, voices carry. I hissed back, "Well, of course not! I only knew you were going off yesterday." It was badly phrased, for if anybody was going off anybody . . . "They're all in the post. Everything. I gave the parcel to the postman first thing. They should be there tomorrow. How are you?" I hoped he might think the anxiety in my voice really was for him. Not that I wasn't concerned. Of course, I was. Humphrey might now be wearing the red shirt, the green socks and that vital pyjama cord. And my husband might be undergoing inspection and injection, laid out flat, propped up with pillows, piped and dripped and drained and sedated, or whatever they do in places like that after journeys like his.

Impatiently, he said, "I'm OK. But I want my things. It's a great pity you couldn't bring them. Sister said . . ."

"Bugger Sister," I said rudely, forgetting my role of languid elegance, "you know bloody well I couldn't. You understand that without me going into it all again. You don't even mind until someone else hints you should. Anyway, I have a customer waiting and I'll have to ring you back if you want a really good go at me. He's leaving *two* dogs so I may be able to stop eating nettles and berries by Friday." He's always on about taking advantage of Nature's Bounty, and once or twice actually cut nettles, boiled them and (I suspect) threw them away with relish. I never saw him actually eat them, not after we murmured about the dogs liking that patch on three legs. Personally, I don't trust nature an inch. Give me a cabbage from the Corner Shop any day. I'll eat mushrooms from Marks and Spencers, never from my own meadow. It might come to that now, of course, but if so, I would fully expect to be the next for the drip-and-drain routine.

The patient muttered something and slammed down the phone. I found I was trembling. Why was it we bickered on the phone when it was something we never, never did at home? Was it merely strain? Frustration? Anxiety? Disappointment? My nose was full of tears so I paused for a moment in the kitchen before going back to play another role – this time Charlotte Rampling men underfoot in scorn with my own despicable toes.

I thought for the millionth time that only dogs would understand without yapping at me. I glanced lovingly at old Rover. He was asleep in his box. He was very quiet; very still. I went over and with eyes aching to cry, knelt to straighten his blanket. There was something different about him that made my heart lurch. Upstairs, I could hear Bustle yapping at a bird through the balcony. The heat had lulled the rest of the dogs into dreams of cool woods and wildlife – or butchers and sausages or whatever it is that makes animals twitch and whimper with excitement in sleep.

Rover was so still. Much much too still. Even sleep creates minute vibrations. But there were no vibrations. There was nothing. Just a dry nose, closed eyes, that terrible stillness.

I drew back, whispering to myself, "Oh, no, God, no . . ." And then, shuddering with horror, I tried to shake a spark of response from the old head. Nothing happened. I pleaded, " . . . don't, please, let him be dead." But it seemed obvious that any prayer at all was going to be a bit late.

I crouched there, shocked into immobility, staring at what was left of a long and faithful life. Memories of his master's eyes disturbed me more than the inevitable end, which no one could have prevented. I would have done anything to put back the clock, breathe a spark of life, however tenuous, back into the failed heart. Shaking and shivering with a dozen different emotions, I took the grizzled head in my hands and covered his mouth with my own, gently blowing down his throat. I did it with sick reluctance and for one reason only. Well, two. Neither very creditable. The first to be able to claim in all honesty I had done everything possible: the second because I was too much of a moral coward to face the old man with the news. It was easier to tackle something physically repellant (and it was) than anything emotionally devastating (as it would be).

Sickness swept over me as the dog's saliva covered my face, but I carried on and on until the limp head fell back among the folds of blanket. I staggered to the sink, retching, and rinsed out my mouth again and again. I gargled, washed my face over and over, scrubbed my hands as if death were contagious. Then I took a clean blanket and draped it right over the box which was still standing in a line from the door where his last days had been spent waiting, watching for someone who might come. But never did.

It was only when I had pulled the box back out of sight, to a corner between the Aga and the wall which had always seemed too stuffy to use, that I remembered who was waiting outside. It hardly seemed to matter any more. I walked out, my eyes red, my hair ruffled, my make-up gone. I could, I suppose, give the impression of having been with a hidden lover, another guerrilla – or merely distraught from the phone call, hearing out, perhaps, the end of a passionate love affair. But the heart had gone out of it. My lips had been fastened only to those of a dead dog and the fact stayed on with me.

"Sorry," I said and sat down. I was still trembling. He must have thought it the result of the phone call because he leant across, looking sympathetic, and took my hand. All that earlier play-acting had achieved far less, I thought ironically. I must remember to reserve any attempts to captivate for the more traumatic moments of my life if possible.

He said, after a short silence, "Something's happened . . .?" His eyes were concerned and his voice gentle. Kindness had been a long-lost commodity. When I realised this, I fell into a deep chasm of self-pity and burst into tears.

"Tell me," he said. And it sounded as if he would take all the cares of the world to his willing shoulders. Hoping, even then, that my eyes looked more tear-drenched than bloated, I shook my head and muttered between sobs, "It's no good. He's dead."

The silence took over again. Then he removed the hand and put an arm round me which was pretty awkward because we were a good way apart and it meant us both leaning sideways so that our respective right and left shoulders still prevented close contact. It was like a prudish aunt conducting a teenage love-in. Bodies do seem poorly designed from the waist up for this sort of thing. So many angles, protuberances, corners. Noses put up a straightforward barrier to simple kisses.

The position between Ross and me was excruciatingly uncomfortable. I drew away a bit, smiling to show it was merely for self-preservation, and gulped to get back a sustained loss of breath. Passion holds its own penalties. I pushed my hair aside and found a tissue in the pocket of my jeans.

"I'm not sure exactly when it happened," I admitted. "Sometime in the past hour or so. It hardly matters. I suppose it was really his age and that he missed the Colonel and his old mistress. He never really had enough time to get attached to me before he started failing . . ." I stopped. Ross was frowning.

"His old mistress?"

"Yes. She's been in a geriatric home for some time now, and when the Colonel went to her at Wittering, it must have been the last straw."

He looked even more puzzled but he muttered, "Awful for you . . ."

"The worst is to come, of course. How on earth do I tell him?" Tears began to run down the side of my nose and fall one by one between my feet. I hoped he wouldn't think it was my nose dripping.

"Tell who?"

"The Colonel when he comes to collect him. Or perhaps I should find out where he is and ring up. No, that's not necessary; it would only make everything worse while he has to be there and . . ."

Ross interrupted, his face clear at last "You mean it's a *dog* that's dead?"

"Of course – Rover – the one I told you about. The one in the box you stepped over in the kitchen. I just found him when I came off the phone. I tried massaging his heart and shaking him and the kiss of life and . . ."

He shouted, "Jesus! I thought you meant your husband!"

Suddenly I began to erupt inside. All the tensions gave way and I put my arms across the table and my head down. Laughter shook my shoulders and great wrenching sobs pulled me apart. For a moment Ross thought it was hysteria, but then realising what he'd said and I'd said, he joined in. It was dreadful, really. With that poor dog lying there, such a short distance away, we rocked and ached together.

Later we walked back into the house. I had composed myself. All the tears and emotions were drenched from my system. I felt like a duck rescued from a thunderstorm. Weak, but safe. Ross had been wonderfully comforting, wonderfully understanding, but full of the kind and practical commonsense I needed. I thought I should ring Hetty and tell her: after all, Rover had been her patient for a long time. Ross said he would come in with me. I knew he realised how much I dreaded seeing the covered body. Hand in hand we entered the kitchen.

Rover was sitting up in his box, the blanket draped over his head like a bridal veil.

I rushed over and hugged him. "He *was* dead half an hour ago," I protested. "It must have been the kiss of life. It must have been delayed action. Well, it must have been . . ." Ross leant against the wall and laughed until tears hit the deck the way mine had earlier.

I went very red. Ross came across and helped me up. I fetched water for Rover who took a few laps and settled back, tail moving imperceptibly. I recalled the mouthwashes, the gargling at the sink. It wasn't the sort of thing one mentions after proclaiming one's impressive skill at saving life. You don't dive in and rescue a friend from drowning and then go on about how cold the water was and how you had to go and get your hair set again. But I did wonder if Ross might have kissed me out there if I had just kept to myself the mouth-to-mouth resuscitation business. I mean, how far can you fancy anyone? Would the Duke of Windsor have been crowned king after all if Wallis Simpson had suddenly announced she'd been blowing down her pug's tonsils? On the other hand Antony took Cleopatra, snake and all. I had to accept that this wasn't going to be one of the Grand Passions of our time, after all.

I rang Hetty while Ross took Bob and Bill for a walk before he had to leave. Bill was as smug as chocolate cream. Both of them were giving me looks of quiet triumph as if I chained them up in peke-sized kennels every day.

Hetty said, "I'm on my way out," when I asked if she would be passing during the day. She sighed as if I was probably screaming for help over a limping labrador.

"It's Rover," I said quickly to show I was in no state of unnecessary panic, "he died. But I gave him the Kiss of Life and now he's OK. I just thought you'd like to know." I hoped I didn't sound as if I was submitting qualifications to figure in next year's Honours List. Hetty wasn't all that impressed.

"Good," she said. "What do you want me to do? Cancel *The Times* obituary?"

I said crossly, "I'm just *telling* you, that's all. You said you'd come if . . ."

"OK," she said, "for Rover's sake, I will, but I shall be at least half an hour so for God's sake keep on kissing!"

It was at that moment I noticed Percy had gone. I had to go into the morning-room to get my sunglasses, because my eyes were beginning to puff up in a most sordid and unromantic way, like a pallid drunk after a party. Willy and Teddy were in there with Toby, all opting for the cool corners under the open window. Percy had been there earlier. Now he wasn't. I rushed round the room, hauling back chairs and flinging open locked cupboards as if Houdini had been at it again in reverse.

Teddy snored, Willy stretched. They both looked a bit shifty. I wondered if they helped him escape. Maybe they saw him – fat as he was – in the terms of a threat to their dinner. Killed him off in a fit of jealous rage. Eaten him to leave no trace . . . After all, it was only one step from pigs' trotters to cannibalism. I decided my nerves were itching up again and began a systematic search.

He would never attempt the stairs. Not with all that weight to carry. He had almost certainly gone off in search of a fried egg or a sherry trifle.

In the distance, across the meadow and against the skyline, I could see Ross and the two dogs, a silhouette of strength. He really was a lovely man. I felt sure he would never have bawled at me about his pyjama cord. Why, a man like that would never even wear pyjamas. But I was rather relieved that they insisted on it in hospitals, what with students and everything.

I concentrated again on finding Percy. Until now, none of the dogs had been missing for more than a few minutes. I knew where they were at any given moment. One call and they (usually) showed up. I was suddenly worried, really worried. Barrel-shaped ladies in tight silk dresses think very highly of fat hairy dogs and are inclined to sue highly for the loss thereof. I had last seen him staring grumpily at his abbreviated breakfast.

He must have slipped through the door when it was open and while Ross and I had been distracted over the living Rover. The door was on a slow automatic hinge. He could have just made it before closing. If anyone had left the gates open, he could now be half way to the village, even up on the motorway.

I was terrified. I paused a moment and began on a few selected lines from *In Memoriam* but it was too apt, and I changed gear quickly into a sonnet from The Portuguese. Elizabeth Barrett Browning, with her devotion to Flush, would have been glad to help any way she could.

Ross was on his way back. I waved my arms at him like a despairing goalkeeper, but by the time he was within earshot I realised I had to appear able to keep cool in *some* crises, at least, and merely said, "That potty peke seems to have flown the nest. I'll have to cast about till I unearth it. I wondered if you could just glimpse round the back of the house while I try the drive?" I like to think the scene resembled one from a movie where the microfilm is hidden in the back tooth of the heroine's elegant Borzoi. No serious sex symbol would admit to a fat peke and for that matter no serious dog-boarder should be admitting to so many mishaps either.

Ross laughed. "OK. For you – anything." He took my hand and smiled. Then he said, "You look as if you had just jumped out of a busy bed at dawn." He had to be joking. I felt as if I'd scrubbed five floors and fallen down a lift shaft. He was on quite a different line of dialogue.

I brought us both back to my own fantasy by saying, "You'll find the secret formula in his right wing molar," and he caught on and said, "Synchronise before we separate!" and that was it. Half time, I thought, if not the Final Whistle.

I decided to cover as much ground as I could, beginning at the far end of the drive where I could see the roads clearly. I knew those short legs and lumpy hips would never get far without continual rests for panting sessions and one of us would intercept the escape before it had gone too far. I scurried round bushes coaxing and calling. I covered the long stretch of creeper-clad wall and the old kitchen garden where fruit bushes had gone wild with freedom from seasons of neglected pruning. I tried herbaceous borders – a mad tangle of thistles and prickles – and the ditch beyond the ha-ha. After ten minutes I hurried back to see if, after all, he was spread out like an old fur collar shedding moths in the sunshine.

Hetty's car stood in the side lane. Two people were nearby, close together, with a bundle between them. Ross and Hetty. The bundle was Percy. Hetty was looking very beautiful; Ross was looking very interested and Percy was looking very very wet.

"I should have warned you he swims," called Hetty as I drew near. Tears of relief and rage reached my eyes. Oh hell! I thought: it's back to drama and trauma and emotions let loose all over the place. If the silly little thing recovered, it still needed nothing more to make this the most disastrous career which had passed under so many bridges into forgotten dreams.

"Where was he?" I took one of the sodden paws. It smelled quite horribly of tadpoles. Percy looked at me with defiance and triumph before sneezing. Was it just that he wanted to get away from it all, the dieting and all it represented? I'd always said it was a mistake. Vital statistics don't matter a fig to a four-legged Fido.

"He's always loved water," said Hetty, "and since he grew so fat, it's given him a feeling of weightlessness. In summer, that coat doesn't encourage normal activity either, but in water it lifts and floats. If he ever goes missing again, look in the pond for a start. The Roland Frobishers call him Perky-poo, it's just too apt when he's fished out of the pondweed." She handed him over. Percy shook so that I was completely soaked. It seemed a good moment to give up emotional roles. Ross and Hetty were laughing . . .

". . . he said you were looking for this great fat peke. I guessed at once, of course, because he's a patient of mine, so . . ."

". . . she asked if I'd noticed a fishpond around the place. Well, I'd noticed the one on the way to the orchard, so . . ."

"Ah! but first you asked why? Did I think he'd taken the easy way out?"

They both fell about laughing. I stood silent and cross. Percy dripped. Then Hetty wiped her eyes – lucid blue, of course, slightly shadowed (Elizabeth Arden probably, I told myself savagely, pale pearl powder) which compared nicely with mine – bloodshot, and bloated.

"We fished him out with your clothes' prop."

"Make him walk back. You should give him a large pan of water every day."

"He's *got* a large pan of water," I said furiously.

"Orientals don't drink their bath water, dear, it's against their religion." They laughed together again. "I mean for swimming about in!" Hetty's pink linen suit was slightly splashed. It only comforted me a little. She said it didn't matter one bit, but I was mean enough to notice with satisfaction that she darted a few worried, sideways glances at the skirt as she went back to her car. Ross went with her as I took Percy, and they stood a moment in the sunshine, delighted with one another. I found a large old towel and rubbed poor smelly Percy with the demented energy of thwarted passion.

Business and pleasure won't work, I reminded myself, remembering the man who bought my herbs and made a pass behind the parsley. I had thought that if I played along a little, business might look up a lot, but we both expected a bit too much from the other in return and the deal fell through in the same way he had fallen when I accidentally pushed him into the cold frames and ruined my pumpkins. You can't get fresh over funeral lilies and we all know what happened when I tried out my charms on the apple-grower.

Hetty came back with her bag and made an impressive show of skill with a stethoscope on Rover. She said he was fine now. She seemed to hint at some exaggeration, even a neurotic death-wish, by me. She admitted he might have suffered an attack of hypothermia from the east wind, untouched by sunshine in the kitchen, causing draughts under the old doors. As soon as I moved the box back into the corner between wall and boiler, the change of atmosphere and the blanket had done the rest.

No mention of my Kiss of Life, and it would have sounded a bit petulant to go on about it. I thanked her for coming and watched the two of them leave together. I was jumping up and down with rage.

I was quite glad to be alone. I organised my obvious stress with a jab of Ella Wheeler Wilcox, gambolling through lines and lines. Unremitting sentimentality is as soothing as hot, sweet tea in an emergency. I can't do with the modern stuff at all, of course. A few dozen bald sentences in uneven order down a page, which would read quite meaninglessly in a straight line, and offer nothing but a good old yawn, do little for anyone except the poet. Rhyming and alliteration, scansion and structure, are all feats to be scorned and dismissed in line with the same dubious asset as being able to suck your big toe. Though I daresay that might be pretty comforting sometimes too.

I had to do something about Marsha. I decided to ring her at once and warn her we had a raging epidemic of rampant acne.

She beat me to it. "Honey," she whispered hoarsely, "I can't come. Remember Ham Skin? He's here . . .!" She waited for the significance to sink in. It didn't, though I did seem to recall the name having been mentioned by her before. "We met again, darling, face to face! In the Social Security Office."

I said, "Social Security? Whatever were you doing there?" She said she'd lost sight of her alimony again and sometimes the S.S. was easier than going to solicitors who had to apply to banks and trusts and things and took *weeks* before letting her have a few goodies. After all, wasn't that exactly what a Welfare State was all about? So one could fare well?

"Ham left the Group, darling," she confided, "and he's drumming along on his own – you know, sort of freelance? Can you hear him? Isn't he just too much? and isn't that the most beautiful bestial beat of all time?" A dull thudding in the background reminded me of a hangover.

"I thought he was the Pole who sculpted sausage-meat?" Marsha got a bit cross and said No, of course not. That was Terse Werd and it was red clay. I asked instead about Bongo and whether he'd had to go when Ham arrived.

"Go?" cried Marsha amazed. "Why should he go? He adores Ham. Simply adores him! He likes Timmy too. They share the same plate and sleep in our bed and Bongo won't want to come and stay with you after all."

Light dawned. "He's a *dog*!" I cried, as if I'd isolated the cold germ.

Marsha said crossly, "I told you – a Tibetan, an Apso. I bought him in the market but Timmy was jealous at first and bit his tail. Bongo hated it and chewed up Tortilla's afghan." I gave a little scream. Most of Marsha's friends kept showy pets but in a block of flats these usually amounted to nothing bigger than a macaw or perhaps a simple snake. Her own place was less than adequate for anything bigger than a placid shrimp, anyway. Tortilla, I seemed to remember, wove grass mats which smelled of stale hay, and she lived in a converted broom cupboard.

"Tortilla's afghan *coat*, you fool!" hissed Marsha.

Luckily at that moment the drumming reached a crescendo and her side at the same time so we shrieked goodbyes and I was able to go to bed satisfied.

The score for the day wasn't all that bad. One bull's eye and a few near misses.

11

By the end of that week I was more or less under way. Established. A viable proposition. Boarders were coming in at the rate of two or three a day – and the bookings ahead were pretty solid. Most were nice amiable family pets, uncomplicated, well-mannered, nicely groomed and adaptable. Their owners were concerned for their welfare, and eager to come and fetch them for odd days if they were staying at hotels within reach on the coast. I was in touch with the resort Information offices within a ten-mile radius, and rang round a few of the bigger hotels, offering Hetty (on her advice) as a reference for recommendations. My cards were being printed, and pamphlets to send out with brochures from anyone who cared to include them. I had spoken again, on the phone, to the grey-haired lady with the cat called Fusty at the offices of the local paper and she had suggested further "small lads" as she seemed to call them, in relevant columns for a few weeks as well as my original arrangement. Everything looked very promising. There was no sudden telegram from Ross's solicitor announcing his assassination, no bad news from the convalescent home, nothing I couldn't handle. Even Rover appeared better. Must have been my breath. Nice to think I had healing qualities in a good puff.

I had placed regular orders with the Pet & Pussy Pantryman and had rung the butcher, Steve, to explain I would be unable to collect after all. It was an enormous relief to be free of the pigs' heads even if it meant other parts instead. But Steve wouldn't be put off. "Hang about, babe," he said in a fair imitation of his current TV hero. "Stevie-boy'll see you all right: I'll be around, don't you worry!" I felt an awful certainty he would be, too.

Lady had taken root as a permanent guest. Adam was back at school until the summer holidays and had already sent me a letter saying his mother was away again and not to worry about ringing her. Cards came for Bustle ("This is Mummy's hotel, Busty-baby, and X marks our" crossed out "my room." Bustle ate the first card, she was sick of lampshades, but the others I lined up for her in my bedroom out of reach.) Willy had kept clear of fits and Teddy had responded to the power of prayer with his placid, patient nature. I began to think I could probably cope after all.

There was, of course, Fritzi, a black dachshund. His mistress, a Miss Pelham-Posford as long and thin as the dog, warned me they both had a cold. "He catches things very easily," she said anxiously.

"I do hope you don't have any problems here. Fritzi got measles from my nephew and had gout last Christmas. You must watch him." I promised to lock up the port. Luckily the flea treatment had been successful or Fritzi would undoubtedly have caught those. As it was he sneezed, and his nose dripped and his bark was positively adenoidal.

Crumbs was dumped. He was a small round black mongrel, and I found him tied to the garden seat when I got up one morning. He was sitting there, shivering because the night had been pretty cold, and there were tears of misery in his wide brown eyes. He was hungry, too. I carried him inside and put him down and he licked up all the toast crumbs from breakfast before I could get him a good meal of his own.

Crumbs was a really adorable little dog, no more than six months old, but he had never been house-trained. This may have been why he was dumped. Training was difficult because of the others around, especially bitches, but by keeping him out in the sunshine a lot of the time, he gradually picked up the rules and after a few weeks he was no trouble at all. When a Mrs Paisley rang up in a flood of tears to cancel a booking because her dog had been hit by a car drawing up outside her front door and had to be put down, I offered Crumbs. It was a risk. Owners might just have come back for him, but anyone prepared to dump a dog with no word, a dog hungry and scared and cold too, had to be discouraged from having one anyway and I was quite prepared to disclaim any knowledge about where he was now. So far as I know, he's still with Mrs Paisley, who often brought him to stay – even for a day when she was in town. She knew he would be happy with us.

When I was a child I had a recurring dream. I was doing a jigsaw puzzle, but every piece was a stray and appealing dog, and every time I fitted a piece into the picture I had found it a happy and permanent home. The dream was so real that when I actually played with a jigsaw, I still recognised the pieces as spaniels and scotties and little round black mongrels, like Crummy. I'm not sure that this proves anything – I don't believe dreams have much connection with reality anyway – but I can see that I must have always had a deep emotional feeling for animals. Or perhaps it was just for anything defenceless, because other people's children had poured in and out of our home when mine were young: not just to visit but to live for varying periods of time and according to need. Nothing so organised as fostering but, now I can see, rather the same way as the dogs came – and went.

The house was full. The kennels were empty. I kept a folded

newspaper on top of the fridge which I slapped on the table, hard, to quell any threat of a riot. Not that it was needed often. I glanced at the date one afternoon and realised it was only used twice in five weeks. Maybe it was the weather that made the dogs languid or perhaps pork is a soporific, but they all appeared to lie around snoozing a lot of the time, waiting, perhaps, for their owners to come back or just dreaming of fun things to do. They looked forward to the walks, some on leads, some free, and enjoyed the hour they had every afternoon in the exercise field. Meals were taken in groups with the slow and fussy together, and the woofers putting it back like dockers in the Darts Bar, elsewhere.

Most of them stayed a week or a fortnight. Some were to stay longer, and some came for a day while owners had to be out. Because their arrival was spasmodic, the others accepted each one without surprise and not much interest. Dogs sense danger and anger and vibrations emanated by disturbed emotions and react accordingly. They make their own laws about discrimination. These are few enough, but bitches seemed happier together mainly because their temperaments were so markedly different from the dogs'. With so much space, this presented no problem and being distributed around made it a lot easier for me. The kitchen always seemed a bit over-populated, but I enjoy that as much as I like a cluttered decor. I had that, too. It's all of a piece with my cluttered mind, I suppose.

Some boarders were neurotic, some aggressive, some just plain grumpy. Nettie, a golden labrador, should have been called Nettle because she was so very touchy. Her owner, a Mrs Broadwater, telephoned me late one night and in a voice which suggested a bomb more than a dog, warned me she intended to bring it over immediately. I was about to go to bed, but she sounded so agitated I weakly said I'd stay up for her.

I lived to regret it. She stayed till dawn broke, alternately sobbing, drinking my coffee laced with brandy and telling me her life story which seemed to be a monotonous string of hard luck incidents. And now, she finished, Mr Broadwater was leaving home. He had dallied with his typist once too often (she said the word 'secretary' was as bogus as 'model' and both meant the same thing) and there had been a showdown. Mrs Broadwater was off to her sister's, but she didn't see why her husband should have the dog as well as the bird, so I was getting it. Poor Nettie wasn't consulted, so I found her a cosy corner by my bed where I could reach out and reassure her during the rest of the short night.

Mr Broadwater turned up next morning, but Nettie streaked out of sight under the bath. I stood my ground and said I could only hand her back to Mrs Broadwater under the arrangements made, so he left Nettie a packet of Edinburgh Rock, which he said was her favourite thing, and went. Her favourite thing certainly wasn't Mr Broadwater because she didn't come back out for three hours and then shrank away from the Edinburgh Rock as if it were doped with strychnine.

A week went by without a word from either Broadwater. Then they turned up together, hand in hand. The reconciliation didn't stretch as far as poor Nettie who had to be carried to the car, protesting violently and howled all the way down the drive.

A really glittering girl came one day to leave her Yorkshire terrier. She was going to Denmark and she cried when she kissed him goodbye. He was utterly enchanting. All Yorkies have a built-in irresistability but this one was ahead of the rest. His name was Bilko and he was a terrible show-off with an aggressive swagger, but only when I was around. As soon as he was alone with any bigger dogs, he hid. I used to leave him challenging Toby or the afghans, one eye on me, and then rush round and peer through the window to see him dive into the back of the cupboard and crouch out of sight of retaliation. He had an endearing way of rolling on his back and biting at his paws, like a very young baby with its toes.

The glittering girl came back with a morose man whom she introduced as her fiancé and I hated handing over Bilko. I worried about him for weeks; I felt sure the morose man would never tolerate Bilko's tricks. Then they turned up again, Bilko bounding ahead and taking over as before. The morose man had changed completely. He was almost vivacious, and when it came to saying goodbye to Bilko, he was far more reluctant to go than the girl, and he was the one who rang every evening to check on the darling's well-being.

On the telephone to my husband, I said, "Eighteen here this week." I was very proud. It showed I was doing my share and could hardly be expected to rush about the country visiting . . .

Pa was not impressed. "Good God! that's a hell of a lot. They'll wreck the place. I thought you were going to make a dozen the limit."

I was speechless. Never had I mentioned a limit. Never, in my own mind, had a limit suggested itself. Come every dog from the ends of the earth and I would stand with welcoming arms – and greedy little cash-box.

I said, reasonably enough, "There's not much difference between twelve and twenty."

"They probably said that in Battersea when the first stray walked in. I don't fancy a share of the Dogs' Home when I'm trying to recuperate!"

I was really shocked. This was, after all, only my usual Rates project, my customary water-wings when the ship looked like foundering. I even had a few ambitions for a future canine United Nations, an example to be demonstrated to the warring human world. Peace among German shepherds, Welsh corgis, Irish wolfhounds, Italian greyhounds, Brussels griffons, English springers – all sharing and caring together. I aimed a well-directed toe at the rear end of a nosey miniature collie, reminding him that we were all friends here and distracting his unwelcome attention from a basset with flat feet and a weak bladder.

I said, "Well, we'll see when you come home, but of course if that's the way you want it, darling . . ." which threw him into the wrong at once.

"Well, you can't be too careful," he warned me. "I was only saying to old Eric this morning" (Who? I thought: there was old This and old That, and Maureen with a chuckle, and Mrs Mountready with hoots of delight) "that rabies can have a bad effect on the sinuses, and a chap in the next room died of canker just before I came down here."

We did seem to waste a lot of time and money exchanging unpleasantries.

I prudently omitted to mention that it didn't end with eighteen dogs. There was a tortoise called Shelmerdine living in a pink playpen provided by the owner when she left a jolly spaniel with only one and a half ears. It was difficult to think up a good reason for refusing Shelmerdine. I could make a small weekly charge, and merely had the job of moving the playpen daily, supplying an abundance of old lettuce leaves and other savoury things. I had the milkman's budgie, Noodle, and two guinea-pigs called Mr and Mrs in their cage named "The Quarrels" which was taped over the front door. This apparently applied not to the occupants but to their owners who squabbled all the time about ownership, turns to clean out, feeding arrangements etc. One of them (a sulky boy of seven) fell in the deep end at Butlins and nearly drowned, but I noticed a marked improvement in his behaviour when he came back. There are, I have often thought, some boys of seven who should be pushed into the deep end at regular intervals to help them grow up.

Hetty's client, the man with the herd of goats, had offered me one in exchange for boarding his two dogs while he was on holiday, and his mynah bird sometimes. As soon as I agreed, he came over with it, carrying a bag of Swoosh which seemed to be all dead flies and dehydrated earwigs.

It was no wonder Major squawked all day. He gave an occasional rendering of Vera Lynn hiccupping through two or three lines of "Now is the Hour" but usually contented himself with hanging upside down ("like a common crow" Hetty rebuked him but I yet have to see a common crow hanging upside down, unless it's as a warning to others over the cabbages) and doing a fair imitation of a slate pencil. Or perhaps I should say un-fair. It nearly drove me insane. Then I put his cage near Noodle's and they both stunned one another into a silence which lasted until it was time for them to go back home.

The barter system was fairly common. The village hairdresser had a boxer puppy I took for a week in exchange for a shampoo and trim; and even a local gardener, leaving a poodle for a week, offered to spend a few evenings tidying up the lawn and surrounding beds when he came back, in lieu of a fee. One dog more or less made little difference, whereas the cost of any service quite definitely did.

I felt pretty organised. Very satisfied. Smug, perhaps. Until Hetty arrived with the goat. I was just moving Shelmerdine's pink playpen.

"My God," she said, obviously impressed, and looking gorgeous in a denim tabard with nothing visible beneath, "going in for the big stuff now, are we?"

I said primly, "We aim to please: my motto is going to be 'Leave anything here, from large husbands to small fleas'."

"Bet you've already got a few of those."

"What? Husbands?" I made sure the playpen had a share of the bush and shade area. Shelmerdine edged sideways, like a crab, towards the latest lettuce leaf.

"Of course," said Hetty.

"Want one?"

She looked pensive. She rarely spoke about Mike, her husband, the engineer who was always away, but I think they shared a perfectly contented marriage. The fact she had an eye for other men only meant, as it usually does, that she was happy with the man she had. One super sweet out of a box doesn't stop you from being interested in the others, whereas one that tastes bitter makes you very very careful.

"Well, there aren't any fleas," I assured her with conceit. "I've really got on top of that. A quick flip through the coat on arrival, a check-up right round every morning, liberal squirts with the dusting powder at intervals, and there's not a jumper in the place."

"There's efficiency for you," said Hetty, cynically. "Rover done any good dying lately? No? Amazing. You should sell bottles of breath to hospitals."

"I shall turn the other cheek and invite you in for a coffee," I said.

"Not till you've looked in my trailer." Hetty had brought her bigger car, a Capri which took a trailer. I stopped in my tracks to the back door.

"Hetty, I've been thinking. Goats need feeding."

"I knew you'd get the hang of it," she said. "Anyone can see you're nothing so crass as a pretty face. There's brain behind the brawn. Yes, unlike the feeble flea who can't find its way around the undergrowth without pinching a bit of you or me, the greedy goat stands back and demands an occasional handout. Go and meet yours . . ." She went inside and I heard her talking to Noodle.

The kid was so tiny I had to put a hand on Toby's collar, just in case he saw it as a handy snack. Behind stood its mother, less impressive if not a great deal more of an asset. I stood stroking noses and making suitable sounds of welcome and wondering what to do next. It seemed churlish to leave them, like keeping a benevolent bishop in the porch while you put the kettle on.

Luckily Hetty came out and joined me. "Rover's OK," she said, as if I didn't know. She was smoothing her long elegant arms with lily-white hands. It never ceased to amaze me that she actually did the rough and heavy work with cattle I knew she did. If doctors could be as glamorous as showgirls in Soho strip clubs, she always said, why not vets? I never pointed out that my doctors had always been unattractive, tough, dull, insensitive and predominantly male.

"How much milk do *I* get and how much does the baby claim?"

"We'll wean her off in a few days; well, weeks then. But she won't need much if we supplement with grazing and a few calf nuts or something. Don't look like that. You're going to be quids in, anyway. All you really have to do is take what's going." The kid, Amanda, had a distinct look of Nureyev, I thought . . .

"You mean – milk them?" . . . pirouetting so prettily.

"It," she said witheringly. Then she looked at me again, "Good God, you can milk a mammal, surely? You a sometime mother, you must know where it comes from?"

I said sulkily, "As a *regular* mother at one time, better possibly than you!" Then I added, "*And* I can milk a goat. We had one years ago, two actually, when the kids were young. My kids. And I remember the time I spent doing it!" And the one who disappeared and ate up a neighbour's washing, and the one who got in the vegetable garden and gave the gardener a mild heart attack by eating every single new shoot. And the time one of them ate rhododendron and kept me up three nights in a row sleeping in a deckchair and sharing a bottle of Napoleon brandy. Of course, there had been moments in spite of the deckchair – but the goat lacked appreciation and died.

Oh, no, I thought. Not all that again and I began to feel sorry for myself. Tears hovered offstage. I felt like a bit-part ingenue with squeaky shoes.

"Milking will probably take less time than chatting up the milkman," said Hetty impatiently, "and you've got a load of untapped meadow out there with one under-privileged horse on it."

"She isn't." We were untying the ropes, leading the goats down. Miranda tiptoed out as daintily as a twenties deb at a presentation. Her daughter, Amanda, skipped and tripped with little squeaks of excitement.

"Where do they go tonight?" It suddenly occurred to me that I was short of suitable accommodation. The stables were still full of empty tea chests. The rest of the outbuildings needed cleaning, at the very least.

"The kennels?" I couldn't think of an argument though it seemed vaguely unsuitable. I said, instead, "What do you mean about my under-privileged horse?" Her name was Harebell – but for some forgotten reason she was always known as Bubbles. Neither name suited her at all. She was a great age, no one was quite sure how old. We had taken her from a rescue society where she was never selected because of her enormous size. She was chestnut, with a white blaze, and a hint of the furry-footed monsters – Shires. She had, when we first took her on as friend and company for two old ponies left over from childhood enthusiasm in the family, been a cosy ride, like a lolloping armchair. Nothing fancy, but very suitable for those of a nervous disposition. Now her companions had gone from us with much sorrow, and Bubbles lived on peacefully, remote but contented. I brushed her most days, chatting as if to a very old lady in her dotage who listens but never quite hears what you say.

Hetty said, "Just because she *may* be a very old horse, it doesn't mean she wouldn't like a bit of light work."

We had reached the end kennel run. I opened the gate and ushered Miranda inside while Amanda, her daughter, bounced about, butting against her mother's side. Hetty and I stood leaning against the chain-link surround, watching.

I queried "Work?" because I thought for a moment she meant behind a plough.

"You could ride her gently round the field now and then. I'm not suggesting the Grand National, but it might do you both a bit of good."

"Let's get some straw," I said. There had been quite a lot left in the barns which had been let to a local farmer while the place was empty. But as we went, I muttered, "It just means more time to find, that's all!"

Hetty said it reminded her that she had to be off to a bull who was scouring its guts out but she'd call in for a moment on her way back. It was lucky for me that the way to her patients led past our gate – or was it? I kept thinking about the bill. It was marvellous to have her dropping in so often, being on call, keeping an eye – however unnecessary. But it wouldn't be so hot when the account had to be settled. The question posed a wall between us.

I went back and stared at Miranda. She looked like one of the more stupid pupils in a class of slow-starters, covering her inabilities with simple virtue. She walked, though, like a brass on the game, hips rolling and with the shock of swinging udder feeling free and swaying immodestly with every step. At least they were appealing and funny – and if I got some milk into the bargain, then I supposed they would be worth a little time and trouble.

The dog kennel was quite big enough for shelter overnight. Strawed up, it was, in fact, ideal. I left them nicely accommodated and went inside to put Noodle in the store room. Then I put Shelmerdine in the potting-shed in her own box of straw (as instructed) and Percy in the porch, because he was being sick, and Major's cage in the cloakroom with the door shut because he was squawking a rhyme he seemed to have suddenly remembered which began "The poor, defrocked vicars, in Rosemary's knickers and he's got your Aunt Fanny in fits . . ." Sometimes he put the second line first and other times he muddled them all up, but the final couplet was always taken at a rush.

"He's got Pamela's petti, and garters from Betty,
With stays of our May's on his . . ."

I closed the door before the triumphant crescendo of the final word.

Back in the kitchen I sat down and put my feet up on the vegetable rack. I took a quick look through the Register, then at the old algebra book from someone's long past schooldays which contained my notes on the blank pages about boarders' little peccadilloes

Daisy, for instance (the unlikely name for a heavy yellow labrador) was down as getting "spongy-paw" in wet weather. If she had to go out for "the necessaries" it said, please put paws in plastic bags. It reminded me that most owners have a sense of modesty when referring to more intimate functions. One had said, "Do watch his widdling, won't you. He has a lazy drainpipe." And another, "If he doesn't do his important pieces by 9.30, give him some encouragement." She meant liquid paraffin, but made it sound like a lazy pianist a bit obstinate about practising.

I re-read the letter from Adam which had come that morning. He said he was saving up to pay me what was due and he added at the end – with what my daughter used to call a 'piss' – "P.S. Tell Lady I'll see her in the holes." It took me a few moments to realise there was an 'e' too many.

I felt a deep affection for all my boarders and their owners. People who care for their dogs and cats – I mean *really* care – share a dimension in character which brings them together in compassion, as merely caring for one another never can. After all, a deep love of animals is the only completely selfless love there is. So I may have grown exasperated, even despaired, of their eccentricities, but I never laughed at the packets of pills, pages of instructions, drips, drops, ointments and lotions. If I was going to be commercial about it, they were all grist to my bill, anyway.

Before I went to bed there was a call from an owner who wanted to know if I minded her Old English sheepdog arriving pale green? I said if he didn't mind, why should I? She explained that he had run past her husband who was using a paint spray ("luckily emulsion" she said with relief). "Scrumpy is so big to bath and I'd never have time, what with packing and the toads."

"Toads?" I queried foolishly.

She launched into an explanation. "Copulating toads," she confirmed earnestly. "Do you realise how agricultural sprays are diminishing the toad population? We must nurture all we can find. These two, copulating, I found in a polluted pond. I have them safely in my drain. I'm feeding them from instructions sent by the Veterinary College, and the spawn I shall distribute to any ponds I can find untouched by the pesticidal monsters wielded by man against nature!" She hoped they would finish copulating by the weekend but if not . . .? No, I said hastily, the responsibility would be too much.

On the way to bed, I passed an embroidered picture picked up in a junk shop. It showed a languid lady in a deckchair reading a book. It read:

"The cow is in the cornfield,
The dog is in the lake,
The pigs are in the meadow, but what difference does it make?"

As soon as I had time, I decided, I would embroider my own version.

12

Miranda turned out to be a bit short on the production line. Even after Mandy was weaned away, Miranda only gave just enough to cut out my milk bills so any wild idea I might have had about providing a local service of goats' milk, with its unique health-giving properties, could be forgotten.

Into the bargain, she was a nibbler. She nibbled my washing, my jacket hanging on the fence, the back pockets of my jeans when I bent over; she nibbled two pages out of the baker's roundsman's order book while he was trying to persuade me to buy Iced Fancies. She also nibbled Bubbles' tail when she was supposed to be keeping her company. After that, in spite of Hetty's derision, I penned Miranda in the old tennis court. Summer's a time for a good swish of the tail against the flies, and you can't do that with a wisp of balding stump.

Marsha had been fairly quiet since a call one midnight when, in tears, she told me Ham had walked out. I was suitably sympathetic, in spite of being choked with yawns. Later, I rang to check whether or not she really *had* leapt from her fifth floor balcony and she said that she'd cheered herself up, down at the S.S. with some of her old penurious friends. She had come back with such a sweet boy who was trying to get a grant from the Arts Council to skip down the central reservation of the M.1 wearing a shroud and using a black skipping-rope. It was to demonstrate the constant presence of death. But so far he was unlucky because of some obscure law about motorway usage.

So he was joining a Group. The Group was going to claim a grant from somewhere to play hymns on old umbrella handles. They called themselves Privy Quickly.

I lapped it up. It made anything I was doing look as boringly unremarkable as selling insurance.

Humphrey called twice a day. He was impressed with my vast amount of mail. Most of it came in postcard form with views of scotties in kilts. Some were addressed to the boarders themselves with fond thoughts, but a lot came to me with messages. "Cuddles to Kirsty" or "Kiss Charlie for me". Owners, on the whole, showed a lot more concern for their dogs than they did for children left in camp or travelling on the continent with schools. There's nothing wrong with that. Even children are less helpless than animals.

Crackers was the highly unsuitable name for a shivering whippet who came for a week. His owner was a brash, leathery young man I disliked the moment he got out of his car. It was the way he looked the house up and down as if its slip was showing. Then he barked orders at the pathetic little dog as if it were a new recruit to some crack regiment. "Heel!" "Sit!" and "Fetch!" only confused it when bawled out like that. It was eager to please – most of them are – but slow in responding, although he sorted things out and got them right eventually. I suppose he probably wasn't all that bright. I don't know why it is all owners expect their dogs to have a high level of intelligence when they must know, surely, that few of their friends have.

The leathery young man ordered the dog to "Stay!" as he left. He thundered out the command and raised a threatening hand as the dog spun about trying to recall what was required. I went inside thinking angrily of Nazi mentalities.

"I reckon any dog should be waiting on command," he said. His girl friend was waiting in the car. She had hair the colour of salami and a frilly blouse that left her shoulders bare. They were very white and deep salt cellars showed where a thin gold chain held a diamond-studded crucifix. She kept calling, "Come *on*, Mick!"

The minute I saw the car leave the gates and head for the coast, I picked up the whippet and cuddled him. I was determined he would have the week of his life. I spoilt that dog rotten. He got the cream off the goat's milk, chocolate bars (not drops) and every loving word I could dream up. I stroked and patted and fondled until my wrists ached. In a few days, Crackers became quite relaxed. He stopped shivering altogether.

I was then consumed with misery about his life reverting to the way it had been before. I decided on a diabolical master plan to outwit Mick the Monster.

They showed up on the Sunday afternoon. The young man was now nicely tanned and wore one of those short-sleeved shirts with bare-boobed native girls all over it. The girl friend was wearing a bikini top and a lot of rough raw red patches where the sun had scorned her skin. I rushed out to greet them, leaving Cracker in the house.

I knew I had to show the young man that merely proving his own strength and power made no impression on anyone. He had to transfer that to his possessions.

"Gosh," I said reverently, "what a tan! and how it suits you . . ." The girl glared from the window of the car. I wondered if she had any legs at all.

"Your car," I sighed, "the sort I've always wanted. I bet it eats up the miles, doesn't it?" It was red and rusty with a half-hearted attempt to be sporty.

Taken off guard, he said, "Nothing special about it. Mind, I tuned her up a bit: yes, she's a go-er all right!" and he beamed.

As we walked up to the front door, I said, "Your wife really is *so* lovely. Is she a celebrity? Only I seem to recognise her from somewhere . . ."

He honked with laughter. "What? Old Brenda? She's my bird, I'm not the sort to marry. No, old Bren works in a laundry up Catford way."

I stopped suddenly. "By the by, did you realise what a real little treasure you've got there? Crackers, I mean. I've a friend who breeds whippets" (it was astonishing how many times I used this bogus friend and how many different things she did and said) "and she reckons he's a champion."

"What, old Crackers? A champ? What 'im? A bundle o' nerves?" but he looked pleased just the same.

"That's only because he's sensitive, highly-strung, all aristocrats are, of course. You must know that." (Slight emphasis on the word "you".) "And he badly needs his confidence restoring. I've a feeling you only got him recently and he must have come from a bullying, unfeeling home before that. Am I right?" Was I pushing my luck too far? But Mick muttered, "Had 'im from a pup . . ."

"Well, you're the man to make something of him," I said triumphantly, "because he really adores you. He was in a dreadful state after you left." That part was true, anyway, but not for the reason he was being made to think.

He looked really flattered. God, he was a thin, transparent great oaf! But I put a hand on his arm and looked up at him. "He'll go mad when he sees you again. Of course, he needs loads of loving and gentle care. But you know that. I don't have to tell *you* that if he's made to feel important, he *will* be important, because once he has enough confidence he could win at shows throughout the country."

I crossed one leg behind the other. It was an honest lie after all, and a simple ankle job would do in lieu of fingers. I trusted to luck that once Crackers was less scared he would be quicker to respond, and once Mick found the new pleasure of caring instead of commanding, both of them would benefit, and be satisfied.

Crackers sneaked up on his belly and rolled over out of reach in terror. "There! What did I tell you? He's overwhelmed!"

Mick carried him to the car. "Get out, you lazy cow!" he bawled at Brenda. "Crackers don't wanna sit be'ind me! 'E's goin' ter sit nex' me in future . . ." and they drove away. I purposely charged more than the usual weekly fee because the more he cost him, the more Mick would value and cherish his potential champion.

I thought of them both for a few days and then other things took over. I almost rang the address I'd been given, but decided I was really better not knowing what happened next.

But what happened next was that Brenda was sent packing. Mick phoned me a long time later and asked if he could bring Crackers down, with his first show ticket. I was dead right, he said, and they were both very grateful, Crackerjack and he. Brenda objected to sharing the bed with a third partner, so she had had to go. As for the whippet, you never saw such a change in a dog. He would have won the Nobel Prize as well as Crufts. Somewhere in that skinny, trembling shape, a real winner had been waiting to get out. I was speechless. I said I'd tell my friend.

I did tell Hetty and she was visibly impressed. We lay on the grass with iced water in tall glasses. It was more cooling and thirst-dispensing than anything flavoured. Hetty said, "We are funny, odd. Both of us."

"Why you?" I could see several reasons why I was.

"Well, to begin with, I set out to be a doctor, like my father (he's a surgeon, and quite a famous one) and found I wanted to do something for the most helpless forms of life. People have enough going for them, individually. So I did two things. I decided to become a vegetarian and a vet."

"That's Odd," I agreed, "but why Funny?" I thought it was marvellous.

"Oh, well, because . . ." she said. Then she straightened. "Have to go and abort a pig." We both got up. "That's what you ought to have – to fatten."

"And you a vegetarian!" I spat it out, hurt to find her such a hypocrite.

"Didn't I add I'm a realist, too?" As she got into her car she added, "I've an idea beginning, and it's rather fantastic. One of my better ones."

"But no pigs," I warned her. "As it is, I shall never eat a ham sandwich again. NO PIGS!" Hetty shook her head and started the engine. "It's even better," she threatened. I went back to the house with my heart sinking.

The phone, as usual, was ringing. Lady now simply stared it out. Long gone the leap, snarl and grab: even the tossed biscuit to keep her mouth busy.

"Hullo?" and then "How are you?"

"Never better," said my husband cheerfully. Then he said,

"Showery here. Brightened up at lunchtime a bit." Such excitement . . .

I countered with, "Strong wind till midday here." Of such is the man/woman relationship, all passion spent. Well, GPO cable-wise anyway.

"Had a card from Robin and Myra," he said proudly. "On holiday. Amsterdam."

"I had a letter from Antony and Cleopatra," I replied, "on the Nile."

"Super." I knew he wasn't listening.

Then he said, ". . . breakfasts good. Porridge *or* and an egg *or*."

"Or what?" I asked, puzzled.

"Kipper. Scrabble in the evening."

"That like kedgeree?" I asked, trying a funny.

But he said seriously, "No, it's the thing played with letter tiles. I got DEVASTATED last night."

I said, "Why? What happened?" I was longing to have my turn, though I knew if I said anything about the goats and a possible pig he'd get scared I was going in for a Jersey herd and a pack of saddlebacks.

We never mentioned when he might come home. The consultant had sent me a short letter saying they were aware we had moved from the area and thought it best to keep him under observation there instead of here where it might be very difficult. You'd have thought we were in the outback at least. We were, I suppose, in his way.

Next I learned that five of them had been to the cinema and had seen a film about an airship run on a fatal fuel that crashed and turned all the occupants into gnats. He said it was very good. I took his word for that.

But when he'd rung off, I had the old feeling of self-pity. I felt bereft. Deserted. Worse, I felt hard done by. There he was with a possible kipper *or*, with letter tiles and movies where people became gnats and here was I, nothing much more than a gnat myself, and no kippers. I wondered if one could get scurvy or something from being deprived of fish. The baker called, the groceries were delivered, Steve brought me "a nice bit a mince" with the offal for the dogs, the pigs' heads and the trotters, and the Pets' Pantryman sometimes turned up selling cabbages with his throats, paunches and lungs. But I was yearning, quite suddenly, for a sprat or a smoked haddock.

I sat on the floor and cried. It was the time one usually bawls at someone, "It's all *your* fault!" I pushed Rosie away and one or two others who came to comfort. They were no use at all for the way I felt. The tears fell faster. I made a noise to show myself how seriously depressed I was. Frilly did a trick or two, like wrenching a harmless flower from the vase on the table and shedding petals about. I still cried. And then, suddenly, I found something being pushed in my lap. Something warm and soft. My hand closed over it with love and gratitude.

It was a pig's head fresh from the oven. I shrieked and leapt to my feet. Toby, in his anxiety, had brought a gift to try and comfort. He usually chose a shoe or a glove or a tea towel, but what gesture could show more love than his next meal?

I doubt if anything could have been more effective. I got up and washed my hands, went upstairs, changed my jeans, and found a book of Dorothy Parker's poems. Reading them again, actually seeing the words grouped together, rhyming and teasing, was even better than a whole page of "Hiawatha" from memory.

It dawned on me about then. Slowly but overwhelmingly, so that for a few minutes I actually stopped still to let it sink in. We were in the same boat, the dogs and I. We felt deserted and none of us really knew if we were ever going to be wanted back.

It had been obvious for a long time, but until that moment I never really saw it. Or perhaps I hadn't wanted to see it. The dogs had a built-in sixth or even seventh sense which gave them courage and confidence and hope. I, being human, had merely an overdeveloped brain which could work out a dozen reasons why it seemed more possible every day that no one was coming back to me. Either my husband was so ill that they had to keep him there for his own sake, or well enough to leave any time but didn't want to come back. The more I thought about it, the more obvious it was. Not once had either of us said lately how much we wanted the other home, nor talked eagerly about the possibility. From my part it was mainly because I felt he would be miserable and grumpy in the undecorated rooms, with the multitude of dogs, the responsibilities, continual activity, barking, muddle, workload, smell of pork, and lack of hot water. Fuel had arrived but the water was never really hot. Maybe the old pipes were furred up. I couldn't afford plumbing luxuries.

I longed to tell someone. Marsha was my oldest friend, but I chose Hetty. I waited till the morning before I phoned.

"Can you drop in?" I asked. "Any time. I hoped this morning . . ."

Hetty said, "One moment." A fusillade of yaps at her end echoed a few from mine, like a slow firing squad in a valley. "That's OK. A patient with a thimble in its ear. Now, what's the matter with who?"

"Nothing much, but it's me. I hate to admit it, but I want advice, and this time for myself."

"Good God," said Hetty, shocked, "don't tell me you've got fleas, too?"

"An emotional problem," I said loftily, but knowing it would fetch her.

"I'll be in after surgery. On my way to the Portly Snorters, OK?"

This was a vast pig-breeding concern run by two big men who looked as if they lived on fat pork. I never did know whether it was her name for them or whether they actually ran it under anything so apt for the sake of publicity.

She was wearing a sexy boiler suit, made of thin cotton, pink. The sleeves were rolled up. We were both tanned but Hetty was dark honey. I was brown.

I said, "Ready for work, eh?" and she said that though ladies in harness need not look like cart-horses they could always aim at a compromise.

"Something like a gay plumber?" I said.

"There's not much wrong with you," she said shortly, so I fetched us each a long drink to cool us down. The summer was challenging weather forecasts and running to extremes every day. It seemed to grow hotter and hotter.

I told her what had kept me awake in short bursts of dismay and longer dreams of disaster most of the night.

She picked up a passing shih tzu, who was staying for a month while its owner was on a business trip, modelling surgical appliances. Then she said, "Do you want him back?" She meant my husband.

"Of course," I said indignantly. But did I? Yes I did. The fact I had to ask myself worried me.

"Look, you happen to be two completely individual people, able to manage your own lives. That's what you've been doing because you had to. If both of you were moaning about it to one another, it would show you each up as selfish, inadequate and insecure. The way it is he'll be back eventually – this is his base as well as yours, however much of yourself you've imprinted on it" (not entirely admiringly) "and meantime you've coped more or less successfully. It would be fairly ridiculous if you piled the agony on one another by yearning and so on."

"You're a bloody hard lady, you are," I said, and wished she looked it, as well. Then we both laughed. I had to convince myself she was right, but it wasn't much help.

Hetty finished her drink and said goodbye. "I'll pop in at teatime, if you like," she offered, "with a few more of my homely words of advice. Such as 'take a Daisy powder with a good shot of gin' or something."

From the car, she called, "How about *hens*?"

"Oh God, she's at it again," I murmured, and then shouted, "*No*, I hate hens." I hated anything at that moment which kept me shut in where I was.

After she'd gone, I watched for a few moments while cars poured on up and down the Motorway, like beads on a pair of parallel strings. The ache to be with them was too much. I stormed in to the house and began painting the kitchen and, even with the usual round of routine jobs, I had the walls finished by late evening. They were a rich shade of brown, drying nicely. Next day the chalking would begin, taking my mind over all the little bits of wisdom again, one by one. Such as my current favourite – EVERYTHING PASSES.

And that, I realised bitterly, meant Life. My own seemed to be a small blue saloon, all windows closed and even windscreen wiper missing, crawling on the slow lane up the Motorway of time. With a flat tyre and no spare.

Not only everything, but everyone, was passing me by.

13

Everyone, that was, except Hetty. Not many friends leave you a pig on the doorstep next to the morning milk . . .

I was coming back from putting Miranda in the tennis court and Amanda in the field, carrying the milk and wishing it was twice the quantity because the dogs enjoyed it so much I was still buying for myself, when I saw Hetty's little car vanishing through the gates. By the tub with the withered shrub was a crate.

The piglet inside was eager to escape. It was nothing to the way I felt. I cursed Hetty. She must have been up at Snorter's very early for an emergency and was rushing to get back quickly for morning surgery. Or was it just that she was unable to face me? I gave her ten minutes and then rang up.

"Oh, the baby?" she said innocently. "He won't give you any trouble. Pop him in a kennel with a nice run, out of the sun a bit, and give him a bottle till I can get you organised."

"*What* bottle? And I don't want any organising, thank you. I don't want the baby either. You can come and fetch him back."

"Well, later maybe," she muttered uneasily, "much later. I've a very full day ahead. Just keep him happy, that's all." Oh yes? I thought, and who's going to do that for *me*?

I went back and took the lid off the crate. The pig sat very firmly on a pile of straw. It was very very thin. I felt the first creeping pangs of compassion. Watch it! I thought, you're going to go all Mother Earth again. I picked it up, all stiff legs and twitching snout.

"You're not staying," I warned it, "don't kid yourself. But you can have a kennel if you like. Well, just for today," and I popped it into the one at the end where a huge overhanging tree provided shade. Then I found a dish of water and the equipment we used for Amanda's weaning, and took Baby some of the goat's milk.

He was honking and snorting and stomping about. Once or twice he fell over because his legs were short of strength. He had enormous ears and tiny little eyes and a turned-up snout and for the first time in two days I began to laugh. I leant against the wire netting and rocked until I was sniffing, my face wet and my shoulders aching. Maybe Hetty wasn't so stoopid and unfeeling after all. Maybe she had a point in what she said – or didn't say. The kitchen was finished and looking quite good after all. (And if you want to know how I did it so quickly, my method is streamlined. *Never*

'Prepare' –just go in and get on, moving pictures, furniture etc. as you go so that they're ready to be put back when that bit has been done: always work in cobwebs and dust for a nice firm finish and make as little fuss as possible. It not only saves time and temper, it makes the work just about bearable.) I looked forward to the chalking. I felt better all round. I even began to wilt over my determination to banish Baby. But not the hens Hetty brought round at teatime.

"Now before you begin," she said, "I never meant this to happen. It's just that it's you or their necks. But look at it this way: they pay for the least possible attention. You need eggs, they've got eggs. Not many, I admit," she added hastily, seeing my scorn. Those birds were missing the first flush of youth along with some feathers and the intelligence to go while the going was good. "But enough for a household like yours." She looked at me anxiously.

I very much doubted whether there *was* another household like mine, so she had a point. But only one.

"I *don't like* hens," I protested.

She gave me a withering glance. "I don't like cutting my toenails, but that doesn't mean I let them grow through the end of my shoes!"

There didn't seem much connection, but I let it go.

I picked up Sparkie, a noisy little cairn. Everything prompted him to join in. Radio, telephone, me singing at the sink. Well, that's understandable, but in a household where there's a background of sounds – even if it was only old Rover's heavy breathing – Sparkie was never without a word to say about it. So, as the others all fell quiet when they saw the brush come out (either from delight or dismay) Sparkie usually fell asleep in self-defence.

"Anyway," said Hetty, "they're not hens. They're bantams!"

No wonder they looked so short in production potential. I shrugged. I was too cross to make any further show of protest.

"I'm sorry," she said. And it was the first time I ever saw Hetty at any sort of loss. Naturally I surrendered.

"You're probably absolutely dead right," I told her, smiling ruefully. "I do need to be as self-supporting as possible, and hens would be the most sensible thing to keep!"

"Good," she said, confidently, "because they're being brought over by Mr Masterman tomorrow!"

I dropped Sparkie and stood up. He shot off barking like a jungle runner with warning tom-toms.

"The bantams are in exchange for boarding his Bessie, a sleepy old black labrador who won't give a moment's trouble and eats anything." If I had my way that would include the bantams, I thought angrily. "And the hens – who really do lay well – he wants back when he comes home from his holiday, and you're minding them in exchange for the eggs *plus* Old Em – or Old M, I'm not sure how he spells it . . ."

"And who is she? His wife? A retired African wart-hog? a tarantula?"

"His parrot. He's leaving Maisie, the cat, up at the cottage and Humphrey promised to open a tin of food a day and check her water bowl. She never drinks milk."

Humphrey's kindness suddenly knocked the selfishness out of me and I said, "I'm very very disappointed about the wart-hog. Let's get these put away somewhere" and together we managed to introduce the bantams into the other end kennel which butted on to the orchard – a very good place for a bit of free range.

Then we walked back to find a drink. Coffee, we agreed, was rapidly turning into a drug for both of us. Needless to say, medlar juice was something for the dreams of balmier days and not even the empty tin invited visitors to be impressed. We usually settled for ice cold water with a dash of vanilla, and if you think that sounds disgusting, try it. Except in hot weather when the conditions are perfect, you'd be right.

Steve was waiting with half the butchery department stacked neatly in cartons in my game larder. He wore a pink shirt with white collar and cuffs, and a grey suit. His ankle boots were of silvery suede. Very dressy, Steve, off duty. He was lying back in a kitchen chair, his feet crossed on the table and his eyes half-shut. Round him Buster, a wheaten terrier, and Winston, a griffon with an expression like an aggravated catfish, squabbled over the ownership of a feather. Bert, crossbred and defiant about it, was intervening or acting as referee, it was hard to tell which. I remembered the feather collection in Buster's box, concealed under his blanket and my heart plummeted at the risks of free range. Something would have to be done for the hens. I could hardly hand back a reduction in numbers to Mr Masterman. If, indeed, I handed back any at all.

"Hi, Steve," I said absently, "thanks for coming by. Like a drink of something tasteless?" Steve neither drank alcohol nor smoked. He was proud of his figure, his energy, the skill he had in pulling the birds – and he had to keep himself alert for his activities locally as a lay preacher. I ceased to be surprised at Steve. He seemed to do everything with polish – he once said it was funny but anything he touched, from women to white mice, skateboards to speedboats, garden forks to the gospels, seemed to be successful.

I made him some coffee. He and Hetty were old friends; they sparred over every subject that came up. I never did know whether they recognised competition in one another or genuinely disagreed. Both enjoyed a challenge.

"How do I stop a cat chasing birds?" I asked them to end an aggressive argument over tails. Hetty refused to do close-docking – boxers, Old English sheepdogs and so on. Steve, who apparently, once bred prize schipperkes, as he had almost anything from racehorses to pigeons, protested it was reasonable enough. "You cut your hair," he kept saying which was driving Hetty mad.

They both stopped when I spoke.

Steve said importantly, "You tie a dead bird round the cat's neck for a week. Longer if you can stand the smell. 'E don't like that!"

"Neither would I." It was on a level with his recent advice on horseflies, steam-irons and a glue for cloisonné. "Anything less offensive?"

"My friend's wife managed to stop her Persian catching parakeets." I should have known better than ask how.

"They drowned it . . ." He fell about laughing.

"Not one of your best," Hetty said. "Do try again. You really must watch a few evening programmes. Children's Hour is going to limit your range a bit."

Steve took no notice at all.

He just said "You could give 'em the feather tick."

"What's that?"

"Mites in the feathers. Like lice. You get one off the bird and put it in the cat's fur. Never try it myself, but they say 'e goes wild with the itch and never goes near a bird again."

I never really knew if he was having me on or not. They do have such weird old ideas in rural areas. Never something practical like a bottle of, or pills for. By the time you've got it all set up, the problem has usually solved itself. Maybe that's their secret . . .

"Thank you," I said, and turned to Hetty.

"Put them in the tennis court with Miranda," she said looking at her finger nails.

Steve helped haul one of the timber kennels under the old, predictable apple trees and the bantams were introduced to the great outside world beyond the run they had been used to at home.

With one accord, a great flutter of feathers and some alarm on my part, they disappeared up into the branches. I thought they'd gone home, or were going, via the treetops. Hetty said, "They often do that. They'll be down later," and she went, followed closely by Steve. I might as well have been left with a team of timber wolves.

I wanted to tell somebody. Marsha's line was busy, so I recklessly tried the convalescent home.

"All our guests are out at the Regatta," said a very seductive voice, female unfortunately. "I'm just going to join them. Any message?" Was it Angharad?

"No, thank you," I said. Not much point arriving like Drake sighting the Armada and bearing the news that the bantams had perched high and would probably drop eggs, if any, into omelettes.

The hens, when they arrived, were more orderly. They looked like water buffalo after the delicacy of the bantams. One particularly had a bold chest and a defiant eye. We settled them in a kennel and I made Hetty sit down for two minutes while I spoke to her like a patient policeman.

"Look, dear," I said with a trace of sarcasm, "I know you mean well, passing me everybody else's leftovers, but I really haven't enough leftover time to milk, feed or fatten anything more. Snorter's runt and Masterman's hens are one thing, but if it comes to timber wolves and water buffaloes . . ." I hoped my expression completed the warning.

"Not bad," she admitted, "but not much good either. I only bring you assets and what does one get from a water buffalo except water? Though I would consider the acquisition of timber to be on a level with eggs from a bantam and probably more financially valuable." I gave up.

"Anyway," I threatened, "enough is enough, whatever it is. I have one pair of hands and no man."

"Well, now, there I can't help much," she agreed. "Let's go and see what eggs are falling from heaven." But the bantams were still up there like a great bunch of feathery bananas. On the way back, with half a dozen dogs leaping round us and Baby trotting alongside, his sharp little feet hard on the gravel, I said, "He integrates with the dogs as if he were merely another breed. I think he's happier with the rest of us."

"Now there you'll save yourself a bit of time," agreed Hetty. "If you let him run with the others until he's too big, you could do yourself a favour too. Much easier for feeding and everything. Just another mouth . . ."

"Are you suggesting porcine cannibalism?" I asked horrified. She ignored me.

"You could fatten several that way. Eventually, with a deep freeze, live through the winter off the summer stock. Vegetables as well as eggs and milk and – well – bacon?" She paused. For a vegetarian, Hetty could close her eyes to aid others, I thought, much too easily.

"I've already got the very daddy of a fridge," I reminded her, "and that's going to need a new belt soon when the Edwardian one finally freaks out." The truth is I can only see a freezer, even now, as one more task force, demanding hours of preparing and packing and storing and then defrosting and disliking. Give me the simple seasonal veg. and an odd tin from the grocer any day.

"You could even have one of Snorter's Portables," mused Hetty, away on her usual cloud.

"If that's another needing daily ministrations . . ."

"It's their speciality sty, designed for weaners. Trouble with them really is they were made collapsible and that's just what they did. Especially when they got a few active young adolescents inside!"

"Thanks, no."

"You could have them very cheap. They're no good up there now so they're selling them off at cost. They're rather into turkeys as the coming thing, anyway. Pigs are finished. You could have one or two of their throw-outs for nothing, maybe." Did she mean pigs, turkeys or accommodation? I really didn't care. She said Snorter's wife wanted a fishpond to hatch trout. It's funny how wives of fat pig-breeders want fishponds. Here was I being tripped up by a pig and a dozen dogs, and there was this unknown lady craving a fishpond. No significance but it just goes to show how very odd we all are. I wondered if Ross Washington's woman wanted a fishpond. Even if he wasn't married, he must have somebody.

"Come on," cried Hetty, rallying to my final retort, "you can do *anything*!"

Flattery makes a virtue of necessity, but I said, "Forget it, will you?"

Hetty glanced at me. "You need a tonic," she said sadly.

"Such as?"

"A day off? an evening out?"

I shook my head and smiled.

"Get a sitter."

"Thanks. It's nothing an aspirin won't cure. I suffer from incurable self-pity. Bring me a bottle next time you come and I'll see what it does" when I've taken the lot at one go, I didn't add, or mean.

"I do know how you feel," she said as she got in the car. "What you really need is a kennelmaid. Now, if I can find . . ."

"Hetty," I interrupted, "I can hardly afford to keep myself, let alone pay somebody else. And even if I could, I'd hate someone here all the time." I suddenly knew it could be true. "I mean, if they weren't exactly right. They might, oh, I don't know, sniff, or smoke or want a bath every day." I was growing so used to warm water as opposed to hot, and to a bath every three days instead of every twenty-four hours, and a quick sponge over instead of a shower, that it now seemed a lot easier than a bath and a great deal quicker. More refreshing, too, in the very hot weather.

Luckily the phone was beginning to panic, so I left her in the middle of saying we must soon discuss her really *big* idea for me, the certain money-spinner. Something I should enjoy and find very profitable. I didn't even argue or protest. I just said, "Lovely: say the last week in October? Must rush," and went.

It was Marsha. "Darling, where were you? I've been holding on for hours. I can't be a moment. I'm expecting my S.S. Inspector for tea and want to make some of those really primitive little buns we used to have at your place, remember? Kid-stuffers, we used to call them. Filling but not very thrilling." She sang the last words. I hadn't a clue what she was talking about. Something sidled in and sat on my foot.

Rosie appeared to have a dead bird in her mouth. For one awful moment, I thought it was a bantam, even the remains of a hen. I dropped the phone in horror but it was a very dead rook. With head averted, I took it off her and put it on top of the dresser until I could cremate it somewhere, otherwise it would become yet another challenger for inclusion in the feather collection, and a bone of contention.

I went back and said, "Sorry. Now what was it?" but she'd gone and the dialling tone expressed righteous indignation.

Rosie was wearing her hurt expression. I comforted her with a crumb or two from the ginger biscuits always crushed in my pocket and patted her. After all, she probably felt every little helped towards the communal stockpot, and was only doing her share. But it was no way to discourage hen-ravage. So far we were lucky because the tennis court was well shut in and the bantams were turning into wildfowl anyway, stuck up the apple trees like partridges among pears at Christmas, but a time could easily come when . . . I stopped there. Left open gates were a hazard of the profession and any small glimmer of smug self-assurance had now been lost among the countless risks and chances I saw about me every day of a precarious life. So far Frilly and the Angel seemed immune to the temptations of ornithology, but if ever they became at all predatory, I could foresee a quick clearance. There was no guarantee that Mr Masterman's hens would go home six and and a cockerel, and bantams are notorious non-survivors. Nature itself was becoming as big in the opposition stakes as the local Rates Dept.

I rang the convalescent home at six. As usual it took a good four minutes to get my husband to the phone. Four minutes is a world warning for Armageddon: an Olympic qualification for the mile. It was also, in my case, a personality changer. From the fond and anxious little woman waiting eagerly at home, the delay made me a snarling harridan resentful at being there.

"That took you long enough," I hissed. It wasn't the greeting I planned.

"They were serving sherry on the verandah – a farewell party for Ted. You remember Ted? I told you about him. He's off tomorrow."

"He's a bit off today, as far as I'm concerned," I muttered, and then through clenched teeth, "Well, that's nice. Dry Sack, I hope? How are you, or do I need to ask?"

"I'm fine," he admitted. "Fell asleep in the sun this afternoon, but I'm so brown now there's no harm done" Oh, good, good! glad about that. "Missed the racing on TV. Still, you can't win 'em all and I did all right yesterday on Postman's Knock at Haydock Park. Did you happen to see the finish? Fantastic! Had a nasty ten minutes waiting for the photo decision." My heart bled for him. "And then lost it all at roulette after dinner!"

"God," I said with feeling, "that's terrible."

"Well, we're running a backgammon team against the Three Bears down the road and I'll admit, with all due modesty, I'm not too bad a hand at it now."

"That's good."

"I had something on Babyface in the 3 o'clock at Kempton. You didn't hear the result by any chance? No, I was afraid not. I just thought you might have been having a feet-up in front of the . . . no, no, I don't suppose it's the programme you'd choose."

"Too right."

"You sound a bit flat. Anything up?"

"Not my feet, anyway." I managed with a short laugh. Cassie, a cairn with worms, rapidly responding to treatment since it was discovered on arrival, looked up puzzled. She thought I was barking. I added, "I didn't ring to exchange hot tips from the stable. It's too expensive. Glad about the Three Bears, though. Not to mention Ted and Babyface." I was aware of being bitchy and no bitch was ever as mean as me. "I'll ring again tomorrow, if I'm still around."

"Why," he asked crossly, "where will you be going? I thought you said you couldn't possibly get away?"

"I was thinking of the next world," I said childishly. "It's the only place I have any desire to visit at the moment. I might get sherry and a nap after lunch."

"Gawd!" he muttered. It meant, "She's off again!" The injured, misunderstood male. Why do they use the word 'pig' after 'chauvenist'? Only men are.

I said, "I'll tell him you mentioned his name. Goodnight." I said and rang off. And then I was sorry.

He rang back right away. I heard his voice and said, "Sorry. I'm just tired I suppose," the age old excuse which gradually shatters relationships and love and even hope. "Sorry . . ." I really was. I needed the contact so much but perhaps that was just it. The vital link seemed lost from the moment I reached out to find it.

"I keep telling you to give up and come down here," he said uneasily. "Chuck it all in. Come on down, stay at an hotel and we'll work something out . . ."

He was solving all my problems – except what to do with innumerable dogs, cats, goats, a pig, birds of all kinds, a horse, tortoise, and somebody's much-loved grass snake called Harriet in a fish tank.

"Maybe. Sometime," I agreed wearily. "It's just a bit tricky right now."

Of course I felt better in the morning. The phone was ringing when I woke at seven: a van had drawn up in the drive and dogs were making a dreadful noise, like the chorus of war in an opera without benefit of supper after the show. And Ross was due to come and fetch the affis. The sun was quite confident about the rest of the day, and everything looked a lot better. It had to.

I wrapped myself in a big towelling bath robe and leant over the balcony.

"What d'you want?" I demanded crossly. Three men stood by a huge red truck, and for one awful moment I thought the removal gang were back to pick up a few items they'd forgotten to pinch last time. There wasn't much of value left.

"GPO," shouted the tallest. I was instantly reminded of backgammon with the Three Bears. Well, it was a change from porridge if nothing else.

"What about it?"

"To do the cables over your ground. We sent you a form."

"Hang on," I said – to them, myself and the phone which had stopped and was now starting again, "I'll be down."

I grabbed the phone as I passed, and gave my number.

A woman's voice said, "I've been recommended by Mrs Haddock" Mrs *Who*? "who left her Willy with you when she went on her honeymoon" Oh! Braddock, and Willy the Fit – of course. "Would you have our Tiddles for a week?"

"Sorry," I said, "I don't take cats."

"But he's no trouble. Just likes to lie in the sun and eat squirrel."

"Squirrel?" I echoed, faint with shock.

"Well, they call it Mickeybits but someone told my husband it's really grey squirrel so that's what we always call it."

"I'm sorry."

"I've seen your ad. in the local paper and it says, 'Let us have poor old Rex' Our cat's a Devon Rex. I could report you under the Trades Description Act." I think she was being funny. You never know. They get desperate when Ibiza beckons.

Outside the GPO men were waiting and inside the dogs were still barking. I said impatiently "OK, OK. Bring him along. Only don't blame me if he disappears: we don't have anywhere for cats to go, except back home," but she was busy being grateful and didn't really hear. I seemed helpless under the rolling tide of parked pets because it was difficult to refuse. It usually seemed hardly worth the effort. Easier to feed goldfish for a fortnight than keep up a running protest for ten minutes. So far as I know, they don't yet have happy Holiday Homes for Hamsters and I never did hear of anyone in the Budgie Boarding Business though for the life of me I can't see why. Owners are often as nutty about budgies as babies. But I'd still rather have other people's dogs. They can't talk when they go home.

The men said a letter had come to me, with a form which I had failed to fill in giving convenient times of access, and according to their understanding, no reply meant it mattered not a fig to me whether they moved in for a day to suit themselves, or a month to make a complete takeover.

It was useless to say the letter, to my certain knowledge, never came. They said so far as they were concerned no answer meant no objection so here they were. A coupla days, they said, eh, Jim?

Jim said a coupla days, too. I asked him if he liked dogs? He said they were all right. He said you could take or leave dogs – or, rather, he said *he* could take or leave 'em, how about you, Dave? Dave could take or leave 'em too. No one asked Cyril, but Cyril looked as if he had taken and left a few in his time, because he was nervously edging backwards towards the van.

"Only I happen to have about twenty at the moment," I said, "and I can hardly be expected to keep them all in for a coupla days: some, of course, are really quite friendly . . ."

Jim looked at Dave and Dave scratched the back of his head.

Cyril got in the van and shut the door firmly. Inside the house, Toby roared like an avenging bull and Mattie like a very large, cross, evil-tempered sheepdog who bites on sight. Jim thought they could leave it till the lady was convenient, like, and Dave thought Jim had a point.

They drove away in a flurry of dust and I went in a bit smug at having won the first round. It's my belief that these jobs keep the boys content but nobody else. Breakdowns have to wait on the convenience of Jim's and Dave's enjoyment of a coupla days in pleasant surroundings crocheting a perfectly capable cable, which is then going to be on and off the blink for a coupla weeks. Until my phone went wrong, the GPO could find another site for holidays.

Success went to my head and I ate two slices of toast piled high with honey. A woman asked me to have Custard (her canary) who needed plenty of company and hated being alone. I said in this place, opportunity would be a fine thing. She said she would bring his millet and I said, wittily I thought, that I'd make sure to polish his beak with it every day, but she said, "No, no, dear, you misunderstand! It's seed, bird seed. Just a touch of Ronuk on the beak . . ." which showed she was wittier than I was.

Teddy, of course, had gone, but his Christian influence remained in a kind of benediction on the household. Lady was regarded as permanent, though letters came often from Adam. At the end of term, he had been sent straight off to France to stay with his father. I sent reassuring news, with paw marks, but felt sad for the little boy shuttled between two uncaring parents when his heart was obviously with the dog. And the dog obviously deserved his love so much more than they did.

I asked Humphrey about Adam's home here, a large dull red-brick house standing in a tree-less square of ground and called "The Firs". It was apparently built in the thirties by a wealthy industrialist still remembered locally as old Billy Bradie who drank himself to death after hurling a radiogram out of an upstairs window at his wife. It seemed a peculiar way to be written down in local history. Not a happy house, even then. I asked Humphrey where the trees had gone and why, and he said they were cut down because they shed cones on the lawn. It sounded on a par with cutting your head off because you get dandruff.

Humphrey was my contact with parochial news. He came in most mornings for coffee, or tea from the coffeepot – no other more suitable arrangement having emerged. In spite of a great deal more unpacking, the teapot still lurked somewhere out of sight. Humphrey said he had one of his palsies. Humphrey's palsy was a sudden shaking of the arm and hand. A relic, he said, of the war when he was evacuated to Coventry.

"*Evacuated*?" I queried. "To Coventry from here? Surely Coventry was right bang in the firing-line?"

"We was living in Norfolk then," he explained. "A little village fifteen miles back from the coast. My Dad reckoned it could be a bit close to invasion, like. So I went to an aunt in Coventry and my sister to Birmingham."

"Birmingham?" I repeated, shocked.

"Well, it were well back from invasion. Me Dad never believed in long-distance bombing. Said our aircraft would have 'em all down over the North Sea and we better get back from the forces when they landed. Dad reckoned they could sneak in overnight on Hoppercraft."

"Hoppercraft?" It was getting monotonous. "What were they, then?"

"Dad had a friend said they was the Secret Weapon. Hopped, like, across the sea and over landmines, barbed wire and the barricades. Every soldier over there was given one. Clipped, like, to his boots . . ." he tailed off vaguely. "Dad was wrong of course: he mostly was, come to think."

"What happened to your sister and parents?" I asked, curious, pouring more tea into his cup.

"Dorothy got killed by a buzz-bomb and I got shock from shrapnel when the local ammunition works was hit. My parents were OK though." The horrors of war and ignorance and gossip.

We changed the subject. "You got a nice Saddleback there," he began again. I straightened automatically, then recognised the breed.

"I thought he was a Lancashire Hot Pot."

"Lincolnshire Odd Spot, you mean," he corrected me. It stil sounded wrong.

"Let's settle for Saddleback," I suggested, gently fondling it ears.

"Lives in, does it?" he asked mildly, storing up a bit of news fo his next call. I dreaded to think how I was being written off roun the village.

"Not exactly," I said with a deprecating smile, "just comes in fo a cuddle and some tea, like you do . . . well, the tea, I mean."

With his mind on this choice bit of local gossip, and his plastic ey fixed crooked, he got up rather quickly and went, leaving me t open my mail. The first letter was from the Bank Manager, askin when I was going to do something about my overdraft.

Such silly questions they ask. Anyway, I thought I *was* doing something about it, although when I wrote to them, enclosing cheques to be paid in, and trying to hit the right note between optimism and efficiency, I did tend to sound rather as if I were making a contribution to their Pension Fund. The Bank Manager had little touch with reality. He failed to appreciate my attempts to relieve his anxiety which, if anything, was a lot greater than mine. I mentioned several possible channels to solvency, such as my mother's old schoolfriend who promised to leave me her silver teapot when she died. Useful as it would undoubtedly be at this point in my life, he was quite welcome to have first refusal when the time came. I also pointed out that I was having a go at the competition on the Fire-lighter packet and would sell my Dream House plus Fitted Carpets the minute I got them. I was also waiting for five Premium Bonds to come up. Capricornians, I once read, are lucky every seventh year and I had at least twenty-one years outstanding. I thought the letter sounded quite promising as I wrote it, but I tore it up after signing it. All the Bank Managers I ever knew, but one, had no sense of humour.

There were cards for the dogs: "Mummy sends licks and wags" left nothing to the imagination, and "Love to the kind lady" was a nudge and wink if ever I saw one. A letter from a friend holidaying in Italy had the usual signs of a fraught conscience. ". . . the trouble is," she wrote, "*men*. My dear, they *never* leave one alone! Worse than gnats in Norfolk. Do anything for you, of course, but you don't *know* how lucky you are in your isolated snugaway." I puked and seethed at the same time. I could have done with just one man to help me lug the sack of dog meat to the larder, and sort it through before sun-up. I read on: "The weather is so hot even iced martinis steam in the shaker. Sleep is impossible but as we seem to have a carnival or fiesta every night and never get to bed till 3 . . ." I tore the letter up and put the pieces down the loo. I'm sure she was in Bognor.

On a plain postcard, a firm offered to give me top prices for old spectacles, paperbacks and dentures. I liked that one better. I wondered if I ought to forward it to the bank. There was a TV licence reminder and an appeal from the RSPCA. I had no TV connected and the RSPCA should have been helping me. No bills though. I did seem to be heading for solvency. The surge of relief was immediately followed by dismay. Once there was no actual necessity for what I was doing, would it just fizzle out like an overloaded barrel being emptied in a drought? Worse than overwork was under-achievement through lack of purpose. There was, of course, the house and garden to organise. Hardly a life's fulfilment. And would it be just for myself? Pa and I seemed to have stopped talking about being together again. And then, with more relief than dismay, I remembered Hetty's mounting account. I would have to go on working to settle the nightmare when she eventually revealed it. Even indirectly, Hetty always seemed to have the answer somehow.

14

First I had to find out just how bad things were down there in the vaults of our bank. I sat in the office to make myself feel more serious about it, and again wrote to the manager. I said that as I was now in business, as well as trouble, he might like to consider opening a second account for me on which I would be able to raise a second overdraft. I didn't add that this way we could transfer the trouble to the business which they always like a lot better than thinking you may be just spending it all on shoes.

The letter held little confidence and even less hope, so I tore it up and tried ringing him. I do believe in the personal approach. I also believe in old things like feminine wiles and the "little woman" act when I'm desperate. Other times I'm a very staunch liberationist. There's a lot of us about.

His name was Bob Wallaby, or so I deduced from his rather dissolute signature. I asked for Mr Wallaby, reminding the clerk I was speaking from seventy miles away. It must have impressed him with the wonders of our mechanical age, because there was a very long pause while it sank in. I could hear the clattering of machinery and teacups: the hum of voices and a radio. I tried not to watch the minute hand on the clock. In about fifty-five seconds I'd lost my patience, temper and nerve. I was just about to replace the receiver when a man's voice said, "Good afternoon?"

"Bob Wallaby?"

"Who?"

Through clenched teeth I repeated, "Mr Wallaby."

He said, "One moment . . ." and I screamed, "*Don't go!*" but he was gone.

I decided to double up the overdraft on the new account just to pay for the call about the old one. He came back eventually, swallowing the crumbs of a Kup Kake and said, "Are you sure you have an account with us?"

"Quite sure, unless you've been handing out my money to casual callers for the past fifteen years." I tried to remain calm. I had not, of course, had so much an *account* as an *overdraft*. I wondered if that would help. I decided it wouldn't.

He said, puzzled, "But we don't have a Wallaby."

"No," I said gritting my teeth again, "your Manager's a Wallaby!" It was a wild accusation. I wasn't surprised when he said coldly, "Our Manager's a Mattingley. You're the Wallaby!"

I disputed this at once. I was not, and never had been. Who was *he*?

He said he was Mr Lyon, Deputy Manager, but at that moment Rover gasped, and I put down the phone to rub his chest. It now seemed to be the right thing to do during Last Moments.

I didn't expect them to hold on and wait for me, so I wrote to Mr Mattingley and said the bank couldn't really afford my phone calls to them and would they please try one to me. But of course they never did. It was just as well, I suppose. I might have gone mad and bought myself an eggtimer or some Bourbon biscuits. And it would only have to be paid back in the end.

The End. The words were ominous. With Hetty's bill hovering, I had a feeling it wasn't far off. I wished I'd gone back into Ladies Alterations which had once made me rich in a week after we moved to a house where we found stacks of writing paper headed "MAID MARIAN". There was nothing to show what Marian made so that left me free to become a fashion designer, a couture stylist, a milliner. The field was wide open for scoping. I decided to cash in on the ever-changing hemline and be an Alterations Expert. It's quicker than the Hardy Amies' route. I put an ad. in the evening paper offering a 24-hour service with collection and delivery. (My husband suddenly grew terrified the Tax Inspector was watching, waiting for even the tiniest profit to show although, knowing me as he did, I doubt the man wasted his time that way. I feel almost as sorry for the taxman as I do for myself.) Constant callers might be suspect.

How was I to know that within a couple of days skirts would take one of their sudden leaps? I was snowed under with gored, flared and circular. I was already loaded with coats, capes, jackets, corsets, slips, dresses and even bras. I was up night and day for a week and the cost in taxis was phenomenal. If the taxman *had* been watching, I reckon he would have been in to offer help. Then the machine and I collapsed together (no doubt with some of my alterations) and I decided on early retirement. The daft thing was I never did get round to using one single sheet of the Maid Marian paper. But that had been in a town where all things are possible, except boarding dogs.

I was just about to try and catch up on the day's routine when the phone rang and Pa said, a bit penitent, I thought, "Hullo, how are you?"

"Fine." I always said Fine. I'm not sure what it means. "And you?"

"Well, OK really. But they say I've got something they want to take a closer look at, so I'm back in bed today."

"Something? Something such as what?"

"Something interesting, the nurse said." I could hear him smirking.

I muttered, "Boasting again!" but I did feel a bit concerned, until he said:

"Still, I can go to the regatta this afternoon." So I stopped worrying. I could hear cries in the background of ". . . come on!" "Bottoms up!" and much laughter.

I said suspiciously, "Where exactly are you?"

"A daybed on the verandah. Some of them are waiting injections, like me. Some off to the town." I wondered which I could hear.

"Well," I said, "let me know what they find. And have fun this afternoon. I'm a bit behind with the work myself."

"Didn't have a letter from you this morning. Keep me up with the news! I like to get something besides dirty Get Well cards from Joe and Trish. Had a parcel from the Simpsons. Nice of them but don't really need *more* books and magazines and sweets. There's plenty of it here. Still, nice of 'em . . ."

"Send some on to me!" I cried through tears of rage and above what appeared to be a boarding party ahoy a battleship, all guns firing, at his end. And I wish they had been firing *at* his end, I really do.

He laughed. "Keep on taking the tablets, as Satan said to Moses!" He roared with laughter. Obviously an in-joke around the wards there – if they *had* wards. It sounded more like Butlins to me. Still, I told myself, I was glad he was having such a pleasant time. Then I told myself, I was close to being a liar.

There was a call later from Ross, expected at teatime. He would have to put off his call to collect for a few days. He would explain later. He hoped it would not be inconvenient. He sounded detached. I hoped I sounded detached. My heart was detached, anyway. I realised how much I looked forward to seeing him again. Men in my life had been narrowed down to palsied, wall-eyed Humphrey, and know-all Steve. You can't count casual callers such as Jim and Dave and the hen-ridden Mr Masterman.

The afghans were no trouble whatsoever except for their coats, but both enjoyed any attention. I do think you could have drawn their teeth without anaesthetic and they would have lain back and looked regal. Concerned with their own inner satisfaction at their outer beauty, they were completely hypnotised against the worst of the world and its opinions. Toby was following me about again, since the Angel had attached herself to Frilly. Toby was my bodyguard, my comforter and if he occasionally tripped me up or ran into me when I stopped suddenly, it was nice to have the reminder of his constancy. R. Shane made no contact at all. I almost hoped it was a case of dumping.

As for Rover, he seemed to hover grimly on the brink of eternity. The Colonel rang sometimes, but his hearing was poor and he monopolised the brief conversation which merely covered the fact he would be away a little longer and he was grateful if we could keep Rover until he came back. We were not sure we could keep Rover until he came back, but we had to sound as if we could.

I was just wondering why I made scones and small cakes for tea as Ross was about the last person to be impressed by a tray cloth, when the groceries arrived. The older Miss Priddle was delivering for a change. I whisked back the best cups and asked her to come in and share.

The Misses Priddle had become my only other friends, apart from Hetty. From the phone call with my order, and the visits they made with the goods, we somehow struck up an understanding which prompted them to pop things in when some Special Offer might have been missed by anyone who couldn't call and actually see it, like me. For my part, I lent them my sewing-machine for their new curtains and my typewriter when theirs was in for overhaul. I advised Miss Maidie Priddle about tomatoes, and Miss Ursula Priddle left me her best suit to alter for a local wedding. It was Miss Ursula who came in and sat with me at the kitchen table with its very unlikely lace-trimmed tray of tea. She was tall and very thin, parcelled in nutty tweed.

"Too windy outside," I said, "and more cosy here."

She looked round. "I do like this room," she said, as if it showed how depraved she was, "and you've got a new one up I see." She was referring to my homespun advice in chalk. It was "NEVER BUY THE JUMBO SIZE. WHO KNOWS HOW LONG YOU'LL BE ALIVE?" and I hoped it would save me from extremes to which, alas, I am prone.

I blushed. "Not to be taken literally in groceries," I said apologetically. "Really a reminder about overdoing things in a roundabout sort of way."

"You do too much, don't you?" she said reprovingly. "And that's why Maidie and I, well, it's why we can't ask you what we had in mind to ring up and say last night."

I had no idea what she was talking about but I knew perfectly well that very few people do too much. They work to capacity, but that's never too much unless they drop with exhaustion and that's pretty rare nowadays. Anyway, there were innumerable compensations and it's no good just seeing the pylon in a field of buttercups.

Activity and no excesses meant I had lost half a stone which, in turn, not only pleased me but gave me further energy. The marvellous summer decorated the world outside so well that it seemed a waste of time to try and compete with anything I could do to the rooms inside. I had a tan that nowhere short of the Sahara could have bettered and my hair was bleached and streaked by the sun with as much success as a Sassoon session could achieve. Even Humphrey had said I was "perking up no end".

"What *were* you going to say, anyhow?" I asked, curious.

"We wondered, Maidie and me, whether you could . . . well, help us out." She paused, embarrassed. I peered fearfully through the window at the van outside. Not a sign or sound of fur, feathers, hide or hair, thank goodness. I didn't owe anything, either. So?

"It's a lot to ask," she murmured. It was the way people begin when they have a leaky puppy they want you to have while Grandma stays the weekend. I wondered if she was going to offer me a part-time job at the shop. I could just see myself there, with Toby clouting cans and cabbages all over the place, Rover dying under the counter and the afghans debating a stiff-legged walkout. I looked doubtful.

"You only have to say No, dear. We know you're more than busy already. We know how marvellous you are," (flattery turns the key) "and how kind." I tried to assume modesty with such earnest endeavour that I might have been suggesting I often shot a few of my boarders on the side to keep the numbers down. "And you do have a lot of space here. You see, it's our Ben." She stopped and looked at me warily. I wondered if I was expected to blench and fall in a heap. But who or what was Ben?

If he was a scottie or pom she would have no trouble coming right out with it. He had to be some great hairy monster with sharp teeth. Their guard dog, probably. Trained to the kill. He'd eat me out of house and home all summer, never hesitate to take a bite at me when trotters palled, and in exchange she would offer discount on his Doggychox. But I couldn't risk offending the dear things.

"I'd love to," I said dishonestly. "You know that, but I'm simply crammed to the rafters. Not an inch anywhere." Frilly sat listening. She always sat very still and took in everything that happened. I often wondered if she was part of the Inland Revenue. Over in the field, Mattie led a small posse on a High Noon confrontation with a rabbit warren. The rest had taken a siesta. I always admire the content and wisdom of dogs. The ability to switch off, relax, detach. They have two worlds, the real and the fantasy and when they despair of one they slip easily and immediately into the other. It beats holidays in Benidorm to a cocked hat.

Miss Priddle was saying, "No, dear. Ben's our nephew."

"Oh, no!" I spluttered. "I have to draw the line at humans!"

She smiled rather sadly. "Ben's not all that human."

It was worse than I feared. "I'd love to help . . ." I began, but she interrupted.

"My brother, his father, works abroad. Ben's mother has never been very strong. The pressures of managing on her own with Ben in London have been building up and now she's had a breakdown. She's in a, well, a suitable hospital . . ." She hesitated. "And I had to go down and bring Ben back with me. But he's not very good in the shop" (or anywhere else, I thought grimly, except on the soccer terraces) "and we don't even have a spare room. He's thirteen and the sofa really is too short. We *are* getting a camp bed, but it's all so difficult in our tiny cottage next to the shop." I knew two of the rooms had been taken over for stock. I began to feel sympathy dissolving into surrender. It kept happening and what had I got? A cat in the kennels, bantams up a tree, hens in the tennis court and a pig in a poke – or the kitchen.

"He could be a great help to you, dear," she tried anxiously, "because he loves animals. He eats a lot, of course" (well, he had a choice here) "but he can get his own meals. He's had to at home, you see. He likes very simple things, like cereals and fruit so he's easy enough to cater for" (and expensive) "but we would pay to cover all that, of course. In fact, his father has already been on the phone and suggested £12 a week, but as well as that we would send up your order on wholesale terms and his own requirements free as our contribution." I stared at her. It was the answer to everything. It was riches beyond compare. OK, so it wasn't the Pools or first prize in the Firelighter competition, but it was a light at the end of a tunnel.

She went on. "We suggest you both try it for a week." I was still silent with surprise. "And no charge for anything until it's settled." She sounded desperate. "Or anything else you can think of."

I felt like Amin with a cowering prisoner promising his toenails.

"It's all too much," I said at last. "Look, let's go through it slowly. He's how old? Thirteen?" She nodded. It was an apology and a plea.

"It's a difficult age" she agreed. Though it's probably easier than thirty when all's said and done. Only all is rarely said and never done.

"He's a bright boy. Why not meet him and see how you feel about it then?"

We agreed he should come to tea and if he hadn't set fire to the foundations or smoked pot in the parlour before he left, he could come back for the rest of his holidays. By which time I would probably be the one with the breakdown.

It was the money which made me give in, of course. I'm not that noble and self-sacrificing. The very fact of it being a regular income, however limited, appealed to me. I'd willingly surrender the guarantee of a future fortune to an agreed immediate weekly pittance. I'm as secure as an untethered tent.

When Miss Ursula had gone, I rang Hetty. Well, I had to tell somebody and she was always the one urging me to expand my horizons. Hetty was on her way out somewhere. She was always coming or going. Her doorstep must have been worn to a wafer. I told her quickly about Ben. She said, "Hey, didn't you tell me you'd never let rooms? That you hadn't time for human beings?"

"I'm not letting rooms," I protested. "I'm looking after one thirteen-year-old inhuman boy." I added as a defence, "Who on earth would take a room in a neglected old ruin with a pack of running rioters?"

Hetty said darkly, "I know a lot of people who love being in unique surroundings, however awful. They pay to go on safari, don't they?" She paused, her mind tapping keys. "How about coming to dinner now you've got a sitter?" She was already converting my gazebo for the intrepid.

"I'm the sitter for *him*, idiot."

"Oh, well, please yourself."

She sounded annoyed so I said quickly, "You come and have dinner here and meet him. I'd like that. I'll get out the Crown Derby and Bristol Blue. I can't guarantee my cellar though . . ." One half pink plonk?

Hetty laughed. She said she wouldn't tell me what I could do with my Crown Derby and she always brought her own Bristols. She could be quite vulgar at times, I said reprovingly, but adding a low comment of my own. Our conversation got steadily worse and I came off the phone resigned to chainstore plates and my half-dozen pack Crystal-Clear Superior Wineware.

Ben was just as Miss Ursula had described him. Thirteen. Other than that I was right, too. A great hairy monster with sharp eyes and prominent teeth, but he seemed harmless. His hair fell to his shoulders and he wore a tee shirt which warned "GET ME, I'M A PUNK" across the front. His tight jeans were a second skin but I daresay the coming generations will be born already kitted out that way. His voice crackled a bit but was pleasant and there was no tedious accent to interpret. How he sounded mattered a lot more than now he looked. You can keep eyes averted but not ears, and a continual mumble or a non-stop squeak is more wearing than war. He picked up one of the dogs when he came in and carried it round with him, talking to me and stepping automatically over the others as if to the hazard born. He only tripped once, when Suki-poo, a sinister puglet, timed it to stand up suddenly and with obvious evil intent. Most people edged nervously about the floor keeping clear of anything bigger than a baby bassett, generating an uneasiness where all had been repose.

"Get out, you silly horse," Ben muttered to the pug. I sighed with relief. Round one to the Misses Priddle. Round two to Ben and Round three, I hoped, to me.

We sat outside and talked. About Fulham next season and how to avoid Art. I said that Fulham would have to strengthen its attack and I'd heard they were going to bring back Bob again. Most teams have a Bob or an ex-Bob: they all need attack. I said Art was only another way of exercising the mind, like Geometry. He said he hated Geometry too. I said sagely that it had its uses and I once called a dog (a bulldog, actually) Isosceles (Sausage for short, of course) because of its back view. He looked at me with something like respect.

He said it was mostly the form master he hated, not the lessons so much. I nodded. When he said he wished his father would come home, I was lost for words and merely waited. Frilly climbed on his knee and a poodle limped round the corner and had to have its paw inspected.

We wandered up to see Bubbles and Miranda. Baby followed with a selection of his friends. Suddenly Ben said, "It's smashing here." Few words have thrilled me more. This plus £12 plus corn flakes. Then he added, "And that's about the best view I ever saw," and he was looking down at the Motorway. Jeeze, I thought, this is it. Love all round at first sight. We would, indeed, live happily ever after. Or at least until the end of the holidays. Ben was better than human.

By evening he was installed, plus bike and kinkajou. It was called Eric and it was the first I ever met face to face. I can't say I was more than mildly attracted. I could see why the Misses Priddle had kept quiet about Eric, because he leapt straight into a bowl of tinned pears the moment Ben put him down. He was fished out and gently shaken and then he sat back and licked off the juice. After that he slumbered as if hit by drugs, and then suddenly shot up the curtain into the pelmet like a duck up a drainpipe in a drought. Ben was unconcerned. "He'll be down when he's got his bearings," he said with complete confidence. I hoped he wouldn't find them for a week.

I had to admire the casual attitude, because it rather reflected my own. No neurotic alarms, no issues and big promotion scenes. We were both so relaxed about living with livestock, I reckoned the place would probably disintegrate under our elbows before we began to notice the crumbling foundations.

Encouraged by the promise of luxuries from the shop, I rang Hetty and told her the meal was fixed for the morrow. "OK," she said, "nothing too fancy mind," and I was easily able to promise that. I wished I'd said a bit less about my prowess at cooking. I was afraid she had the impression of expertise lying somewhere between Fanny Craddock and Robert Carrier. A very nasty position to be in.

The carton Ben brought with him was full of corn flakes, biscuits, bananas and baked beans. There was also brown bread and best butter. I once went on a diet of alphabetical food – mostly Bs and Cs. I could eat cakes, chocolate and cabbage for a week, but not bread, butter or bacon. It wasn't spectacularly successful because after a few days you feel choked up to here with stodge, while cabbage loses any appeal it might have had at the start. So for the rest of the week the point lies in the fact you don't eat anything much at all. You have to look around for other things not too awful, like carrots and crab apple jelly, until it's time to reverse the process and make a rush at the bacon butties. Looking back, I think the instructions needed more careful investigation.

Miss Maidie had also put in oranges and sausage rolls and a jar of pickled onions. Some Liquorice Allsorts and cherry slices and scotch eggs. I hardly thought anything remotely Cordon Bleu could come from that. Maybe, I hoped, Steve would bring me something. He often left a wrapped chop or some liver, a couple of hearts or a nice piece of steak for me, as a small token, I presumed, of his esteem. I always tried to pay him but he refused to consider stepping off his superior pedestal to accept hard cash. I knew I could never cook chicken, not with the hens down there in the dog kennel. I usually fed the liver and hearts to Rover, because since the advent of a spare part surgery unit for pigs in our larder, the very idea of meat for myself was impossible.

I lay awake all night turning over baked beans and cabbage with tinned raspberries and a banana dominating my imagination, until my stomach turned over, too, in protest. But the dawn and the decisions came together, and I fell asleep happy.

Ben spent most of the day arranging his room – the big spare one on the opposite corner to mine, facing the Motorway and with a similar balcony. Then he sat down with my typewriter and began a letter to his father. I turned out a few crates until I found the book I wanted – *Cooking to Confuse* – and the chapter I remembered. I made a short list of extras for Ben to fetch on his bike, but most of the instructions could be adjusted a little. I was much better at improvising than I was at cooking.

The dogs liked to see me busy and happy. Ben was the right kind of company – only "there" most of the time and not imposing anything. He made sensible comments about simple things which were hardly mind-bending, and just about met my own level. Things about Radio 2, and outer space and bicycle bells.

Hetty was due at seven. Ben and I made sure the dogs were bedded down early, the milking done and the hens shut in. The bantams were at last down from the trees and Steve had dropped off an old poultry ark which they adopted at once. By 6.30 everything was ready.

We were to eat outside, so I had taken lamps and draped the shades with pink silk, dipped in the dye with the damask cloth and napkins. We laid the round iron table for our plates, and the long bench from the hall to take the dishes. The effect was amazing. As evening closed in and the lights went on, and with the Motorway sparkling in the background, I felt we would be almost up to colour supplement and Chelsea chic. Ben volunteered to change into a clean shirt and even a tie. I found a long, sweeping dress of lilac jersey silk and my elegantly heeled sandals. With clean hair and the whole cosmetic range, I was unrecognisable.

The pink roses on the trellis might have been made of paper specially to match the cloth. Trailing stephanotis and an arrangement of forget-me-nots decorated the bench and table. I felt almost civilised, too.

Hetty brought the wine with her. Miss Ursula had sent me up a bottle of cream sherry. We drank together on the newly christened patio or terrace, and admired one another. Hetty was in cream silk, she wore no shoes and her finger nails and toenails were gold. Round her neck she had a broad gold band studded with brilliant colours, and a matching ring on one hand. Even Ben was impressed. We stood, strangers to one another, only Charles Aznavour unconcerned in the background murmuring yearningly. We held our glasses at awkward angles, adopted attitudes – a far cry from yesterday. Ben looked remarkably tidy, but somehow even more ludicrous, in a formal shirt and clean jeans. His tennis shoes, part of his permanent way along with acne, teeth and ears, were, luckily, half hidden by the shadows. I introduced him to Hetty and swanned back inside for a few cocktail onions and the dish of olives from a bottle stored with my hostess's reputation among a small group of untouchables at the back of the fridge.

Carrying anything presented a few problems. The sudden air of tension worried Toby who now walked so close that I had to keep my elbows out of the way of his nose by lifting dishes shoulder-high. I must have resembled a triumphant entry – such as the Head on the Platter incident in the Bible – and I was just thinking that could be quite horribly apt later, when Baby raced into the arena, honking with triumph, furious at being put to bed early and delighted to escape. He was definitely no asset to my party plan. He dived between my feet and I lurched, sending a shower of onions and olives into the record-player and beyond. Aznavour hiccuped, the dishes lay in pieces, and I grabbed Baby who wriggled and squealed as my heels sunk in the begonia bed. The dogs inside woke and began barking, while those still slumbering peacefully outside leapt to our aid and all over the splendid decor. There was a crash as the lamps came down and another as a chair fell over. Hetty was apparently choking. I thought she must have a nut lodged in her throat till I saw she was merely laughing.

"Fantastic!" she assured me, gasping and wiping her eyes, "utterly fantastic! A Welcoming Tableau – I believe it was a feature in ancient Rome for honoured guests . . ." and she was away again, at the same time hauling Toby off the butter where his undercarriage rested as he stood over the bench to get a bit closer and gaze anxiously into my eyes.

Ben came over and took Baby. "I'll put him back," he said apologetically. "I must have left his gate unlatched. Would he keep quiet if we put Amanda with him? or Rosie?"

"No, no, don't do that for heaven's sake," I said hastily. "Two of them could set up a whole disaster area." I smoothed down my scuffed silk jersey and shook out my hair. Mattie, usually detached from the rest of us, had lumbered over carrying a freshly resurrected rat from a collection of corpses she kept hidden ready for just such emergencies, doing her usual best to add to my embarrassment. It didn't take much to make it absolute. I noticed without surprise that Aznavour had handed the torch to Sinatra, who was now Doing It His Way. I'd already done it mine, I thought.

Things calmed down during the meal. The wine was cool and soothing, the consommé lightly chilled and the salad crisp. My home-baked rolls were fresh from the oven and the butter patted into a thistle on the block. The main dish was Moussaka Provençale decorated with sliced orange. The sweet, a Gibanitsa. Miss Priddle had sent a solid wedge of ripe Stilton and a box of petit fours. Two wine bottles stood empty when Hetty produced the liqueur brandy. I held out my glass for more.

"Someone," I said thickly, "should be directing a commercial for something."

I felt very bland, very relaxed. Too relaxed . . . Hetty topped up my narrow glass.

"The consommé," she sighed, "was quite, quite perfect. What inspired it exactly?"

"Thish and that," I said, the Motorway a kaleidoscope of dipping and weaving lights, "and, of course, a bit of the other." I giggled. Wild horses would never get the truth out of me. Wild pigs might, of course, but that was to be expected. "Herbs, you know," I went on airily. "You have to remember, I'm speshul on herbs. And I do still have a lot of old shtock around . . ."

Hetty stared. "Old stock?" she repeated. "You mean – *stock* – *old*?"

"Not shtockpot shtock," I assured her hastily. "You know, wholeshale/retail shtock. The shtuff that didn't shell." And there was always plenty of that. My head was buzzing. Was it gnats or alcohol? I shook my hair to clear my ears. Something was inside knocking on my brain. If it was trying to get out, I wouldn't stop it.

"And the moussaka?" she was asking, "how did you? and what did you . . .? and was there . . .?" I nodded and tapped the side of my nose with one finger, smiling what I hoped was a sly smile. When I picked up my coffee it wobbled from the cup into the saucer. I looked round to see if everything else was doing the same: it only needed an earthquake to make the occasion for posterity.

Hetty, accustomed to wine, and Ben, who had been on Coca-Cola, were discussing Eric. I wanted to join in. I wanted to prove I was as sober as they were. I kept waiting for them to pause, but in the end I had to interrupt. I stood up suddenly: I must have been six foot tall at least. I felt I was towering over everything and from a great distance I heard them both laugh. I began to walk forward to get the coffee-pot – I needed it hot and black and strong, but Toby, as he lay with anxious eyes watching me from under the bench sprang to his feet protectively. He took the bench, china, butter, petit fours, cheese and remains of the meal with him in a great cascade over everything. Cold consommé covered my feet and slices of orange slid very slowly down my skirt. Hetty was shaking salad leaves from hers, like a naiad emerging from a lake decked in seaweed. Ben was covering his face with a hand to control himself. The party was over.

With a great dramatic gesture, flinging my arms to the night sky, I cried, "Trotters and tongues!" much as early Christians confessed their faith at the stake. Then, as I noticed smoke pouring from the open kitchen window, I burst into tears and passed out.

15

"Hi!" said Hetty on the phone.

I felt myself blushing. Finding the house still standing, the debris cleared, the kitchen immaculate and my head throbbing, reminded me of things better forgotten.

"Not so high as last night," I admitted, shamefully.

"My dear, it was the Grand Finale, the Great Transformation Scene, the Final Effect, and I wouldn't have missed it for the world. What I call a really spectacular evening. I can't thank you enough for having me in on it."

"Or me, you, for the way you must have worked afterwards. The place never looked better!" It had never looked so good and we both knew it.

Hetty said smugly, "Have you noticed how satisfying it is to put straight somebody else's muddle?" She was doing it all the time.

"It has curiosity value," I admitted. "You get a good insight into other people's shortcomings when you see their most intimate things, like tea towels and fish slices." I looked round, then asked, "What was on fire?"

"Two thin slices in the toaster which failed to pop. Left there since breakfast, Ben thought, and you switched it on when you plugged in the coffee. You *did* use trotters *and other parts* in the soup and moussaka, didn't you?" It was more a challenge than an accusation. "Come clean, I had a look in the bottom oven . . ."

"You said it was good," I reminded her defiantly, "and I'm sorry you had to break vows of total abstinence without knowing. I forgot." It wasn't strictly true. I had remembered about Hetty being a vegetarian when I began to serve it up but it was too late then.

"Look, I'm not that rigid. I've been caught with a hamburger when starving and was once seen with a sausage when I wasn't." We both laughed without much enthusiasm.

And so the dismal disaster was turned into a memory – and another win on the scoreboard for Hetty.

For myself, though, I added half a point. No one else would ever know trotters and tongues were not the only contribution to the minced part of the moussaka. And as I said later, when I confided to Marsha on the phone, with the underlying hope it might put off any further suggestion of a visit: "What's the difference in the end, what's the dread comparison, between flank, foot and face? Yours, mine or Baby's?"

She said she'd remember that next time she got her bum pinched.

Ben was full of admiration for Hetty. He said she had whisked round the kitchen with her dress tucked up wearing the tablecloth tied round her neck and belted with a dog lead. He said she knew everything about kinks (kinkajous) and she'd promised him a desert rat. He was going down to the surgery one day to watch when she operated. He wanted to be a vet, he added.

I said, "Yesterday, you wanted to be a trombonist!"

He said he could always play the trombone when he'd finished spaying cats.

"Whatever time did you get to bed?" I asked fearfully. The toaster was working innocently this morning, and two slices leapt out of the flower bowl. No wonder it rebelled from time to time – Ben would arrange it in a concealed position for the sheer novelty of surprise when toast appeared to jump from the fish tank or birdcage. The trouble was that it so often jumped *in*.

"Around midnight." He piled marmalade an inch high and washed it down with tea. I wished I, too, had been on Coke and not alcohol the night before. I always did say cream soda would have turned Russia into a nicer nation.

I began to dole out the day's pills, ointments, lotions and drops. No one enjoyed it but everyone recognised the routine was unavoidable.

"I don't know what your aunts are going to say," I muttered.

"As long as I'm OK and you can stand the strain, they'll be happy," he assured me. "They were terrified I'd do something to spoil their good name in the village. It all comes down to business in the end," he said philosophically.

"Such as what?" I asked, putting drops in Fido's ears, and offering biscuits.

"Well, you know, talking . . ." Fido took the biscuit as the drops oozed in.

"Talking? Everyone talks." Fido was allowed to go and I grabbed for a red setter puppy who needed cod liver oil capsules. I don't know which of us rebelled at the idea the most.

"Talking about my Mum, mostly I suppose. And Dad. And their shop and all that," he said, his mouth full of toast and peanut butter.

So that was why they had been so willing to bribe me into having him! And I thought he was a delinquent. He was far from being that. Rather a nice boy on the whole if you didn't look too closely when he ate.

"Hetty and I were talking about animal noises," he went on,

making a few himself as he washed down another mouthful with hot tea, "and she suggests I make a study of them, get them on tape and perhaps write them up somewhere."

"That's interesting," I said. "Jolly good. Splendid idea," though for the life of me I couldn't think why. Still, it would keep him busy and with some sort of object in being here.

I got up and suggested he should come out with me and get the milk and eggs. Miranda was waiting impatiently and the hens wanted to be off. "Any idea what you'd like for lunch?" I asked.

"Shreddies and sardines?" he suggested hopefully. I couldn't get back into the fresh air quick enough.

Ben already knew Humphrey so neither was surprised to see the other. They talked by the van while I milked and were still there when I opened the gate from the run and let Amanda out. She made a beeline for the sack of mail and had the letters before I could tie up Miranda and grab. To Humphrey I cried, "Look! Look! A UFO . . . down there, beyond the trees" as I hastily scooped the chewed remains and pushed them back. By the time they turned to tell me there was nothing there, I had Amanda by the collar and was leading her back to the field. Bubbles waited by the gate every morning. They seemed utterly devoted already, in spite of the vast difference in size. Unlike her mother, Amanda never nibbled tails and Bubbles would lean over the growing kid and blow the flies away.

I had been riding again once or twice a week, at first slowly and carefully in the field and then going a bit further. Hetty had been right, of course, we both needed the exercise. But even more than that, we needed the contact of affection.

It was a morning for getting myself together, totting up assets, reassessing limitations. The summer was half way over. Ends were meeting now, as well as being in sight. Mainly thanks to Ben, most of my troubles were over, too, but he would be back at school in September, and what then? The great trek back to work would be complete. The Fidos and Charlies and Paddys would be home again.

I rarely comforted myself with the promise of Pa's homecoming. Neither of us mentioned it on the rarer and rarer occasions we spoke on the phone. I knew he would need rest and freedom from worry until he could start work again, and I couldn't offer that. He probably saw I had a new life I'd been building up without him and felt no part of it. Did he *want* to come back? If so, he never said he did. Did I *want* him here? At the moment, it only seemed an added responsibility.

I detached Miranda from the honeysuckle where she was making a meal of the best flowers, and just hoped she would steer clear of the rhododendrons now growing riotously beyond the tennis court. Honeysuckle would only give her a headache, rhododendrons would give her incurable gripes.

Ben was on the phone when I went back inside. He was saying, ". . . and put in some Kup Kakes to cheer her up or she'll go and jump in the duckpond."

"That's a fine treatment for suicide," I said as he rang off. "Anyone we know?"

He blushed. "They'll send them if I say they're for you, not for Eric though, and I must have them to get him down from the pelmet. I think he's building a nest up there. He's not doing your linings any favour, either."

"Well, they weren't terribly posh to begin with," I said, wondering why I never minded about wear, tear, crash, crack or splinter. Everything has its term of life.

"They hate him, you know," confided Ben. "When he was at the shop, he pee-ed on the pork luncheon meat." I reminded myself to keep clear of that particular luxury when ordering. "They'll send up anything to keep him away." He added, "And if they think it's for you, they'd include the till!" Everyone has their price, as they say.

I got out my 'Books'. They included notes on manilla envelopes and some loose pages from an old notebook as well as my proper accounts. I looked forward, in a perverse sort of way, to the first call from our lurking Tax Inspector, merely to see if he could manage my methods.

Things seemed to just about balance, leaving my labour given entirely for love. Baby was growing quickly, but needed extra food. The hens produced more than enough eggs for two. Free range paid off, except when it was Baby getting it. He looked like becoming a great big boar – and you can spell that either way – while his snouting bouts were developing into furores of destructive delight. Free range, in fact, like Free Love and Free Enterprise, has been known to exceed the bounds of wisdom.

But what I lost on the roundabouts I gained on the swings. Pudding, a hairy, happy dog, in the same mould as Holy Ted or St Edward, as Hetty called one of our first boarders – dear, praying Teddy – was one of Nature's warm-hearted benefactors. He had an eager expression, rangy pink tongue always on view and a wildly waving tail. He was too big to be cuddly and too small to be dignified. His special thing was 'Hide-and-Seek' and he continually fetched things like my purse or wrist-watch to be hidden so he could show his skill in finding them again.

The moment he arrived, he took over general duties. He licked all the dishes clean, rounded up stragglers from walks, led games in the Exercise Yard in the afternoon and completely monopolised the care of Rover. With great sympathy and concern, he would climb in Rover's box and begin licking him all over his ears and face. It seemed a very unhygienic way to carry on. Not at all in the National Health bracket. What's more, he would squash up and sleep there at night, and often at times during the day, completely ignoring his own box near the range. In fact, I think he had come to an arrangement with Spot, a Jack Russell terrier, who deserted his own basket and buried such treasures as a rubber bone and some disintegrating claws, under the blanket which was once Pudding's. I had an idea the claws were from the dead rook I'd hidden on top of the dresser when I was on the phone to Marsha once, and forgot for a few days until the smell reminded me. Rosie, as usual, had later found it wrapped and buried, dug it up and lost it in fair competition to the acquisitive Spot.

The strange thing was that from the moment Pudding started sharing with Rover, the old dog began to perk up a lot. He seemed quite jaunty sometimes, taking a voluntary stroll in the sunshine, or joining in the chorus when a car was heard outside. I did wonder whether our own medical profession should look quite seriously at the benefits of closer contact with physical life for those gravely ill. The enormous comfort of having someone you love put their arms around you, holding you near, willing abundant life to flow between, may have a much greater healing power than we realise. The terrible impersonality of standard hospital treatment works well enough on the body, but there is more to staying alive than muscular mechanics. Actually sharing the bed might be a good idea.

Of course, some dogs are kinder and more considerate than others, just as some are brighter, some are crosser and some greedier or sleepier or have a greater sense of humour. They are, in point of fact, us – a life force – in a less advanced shape. Pudding, for instance, was a dog who never made you feel guilty. If I was late with his dinner, he hopped about in delight because it was coming eventually, instead of sulking as Mattie did. If I brushed him, he rolled over and laughed, wagging his fulsome tail all over the floor and never making the slightest protest at a knot. He swaggered with happiness when he walked. He watched me with eyes full of joy and admiration and kindliness and care. Very few people ever attain such perfection.

Most dogs smile. Some, again, more than others and Sybil, a long-legged Yorkshire terrier who would have shamed a show-ring actually laughed. Like anyone with a pronounced sense of humour, she was more intelligent than most and had a seventh sense which I often used as a warning while she was with us. She sensed rain and visitors and even the telephone, ears pricked before it rang. She had a thin, gingery coat and big black eyes, always a bit tearful. But with laughing, not from sorrow. And when she laughed, her head went down sideways, chin up, uneven teeth on display (she'd been sat on by a labrador as a puppy and had had her jaw dislocated) and, with her bottom in the air, she'd give this disarmingly wide and quite hideous grin. It was ingratiating, begging you to share her loving laughter, and yet endearing to a point where I had to get down and hug her, laughing too. Sybil came back to me later, for good, and only died aged fourteen, a very short time ago. One of the characters I treasure most in my heart and will always miss.

There was now, too, an apricot poodle, called Emma Hamilton, who belonged to the village hairdresser. With a small car, the two of them toured local villages bringing scissors and dyes and perms to the isolated ladies until, one day, some children opened the car where Emma waited with her usual patience, and took her away. They played with her for a while and then left her tied up in a shed, forgetting to go back with food or water. She was discovered two days later and, because of the great hullabaloo which her owner had raised over the entire county, was handed back in exchange for a whacking reward. But after that, Emma refused point blank to go anywhere by car and had to be brought to me three days a week while her mistress was working. She stayed for the day on special reduced terms.

Emma, unlike Sybil, and perhaps because of her nasty experience, was a very solemn little dog and needed a great deal of reassurance and love. I spent most of the time when she was first with us, just carrying her around as I worked. Then she would follow me and finally she took to following Toby. What with Frilly who was always with Angel who was usually near Toby as well, I had a complete retinue.

Growing too fond was one danger I had to face. Handing back to an indifferent owner, I learned, could be terribly hard, cause sleepless nights and anxiety probably beyond necessity. Growing too confident was another.

After the first fight occurred, an element of doubt crept in about my theories and a subsequent wariness which, in turn, spread to the rest. It was now impossible to be sure and very reluctantly I began sorting out the sheep from the foxes. The large and overbearing from the small and defenceless. I began using the spare kennels for the kind of dog whose ancestors were bred to attack – alsatians, rottweilers – for at least a good part of the day. I tried to keep only the smaller toy and pet breeds in the living-rooms, with access to the terrace and rose garden as opposed to the kitchen quarters where they could find their way out to the vegetable garden and the field.

The first fight was a complete surprise. I was making pastry. A corgi, called Bella who had arrived a few hours earlier, had been settled with her basket under the dresser. She appeared docile enough. I waited and watched and talked soothingly as the others came over and sniffed about, generally accepting the newcomer. Everyone had a bit of ginger snap and then I let them settle back to their own business. I was just beginning to roll out the dough when I heard a low growl. I looked down and saw Bella advancing towards Spot who was enjoying a mild attack on some fringe at the edge of the mat. Before either Spot or I could stop her, Bella had leapt on poor Spot and within a few seconds a scrum of battling dogs was rolling round the floor screaming and yelping and knocking away legs from chairs and one another and nothing was upright except me and Toby, both horrified in the wings.

I grabbed the washing-up bowl, full of cold water, and hurled the lot into the middle of the struggle, wading in after and grabbing Bella, kicking one or two others and shouting with an authority I was very far from feeling.

I came out with Bella's teeth in Spot's ear and Spot dangling, and threw them both into the scullery. As they landed, I snatched Spot back and shut him in the broom cupboard. Shaking with terror for the other, less able, protagonists, and seeing myself handing them back to owners in bits, I kicked and grabbed around the rest who were still at it. At the cost of a few minor bites and abrasions, and a thumping great bruise where I whacked my leg with a broom instead of one of the aggressors, we ended up fairly unscathed although it took the whole week of Spot's stay with us to get his ear looking presentable. One or two of the others limped for a day or two, more in protest and with an air of sulky self-righteousness than anything worse. Frankly, I think some of them rather enjoyed it like militant pickets defending what they considered their rights. I put them all out in separate kennels while I cleared up, but I knew with a sinking dismay that the atmosphere of utter confidence in command that I had created and which had been so easily recognised and immediately respected, had gone. From then on my own caution developed a new wariness and none of us ever again could be quite sure of our reliability.

They came back in, of course, but a few at a time and with th utmost care. They took up the same positions of friendly rivalry in communal living, but I now began to weed out likely trouble-makers and watch them very closely in order to avoid danger before it might begin. Corgis, alsatians and occasionally other breeds with a history of ancestral aggression – usually from early training to attack – were the worst, and the occasional problem dog with some underlying fear or sickness which was at first unapparent.

I rang Hetty once the fight was over, the kitchen straight, my hands steady enough to hold a drink and dial a number. She was just coming in and there was an accident emergency waiting. I said, "And here's another," and told her. Then I burst into tears.

"Did you really think you could always get away without any trouble?" she asked quite kindly but with some exasperation.

"Yes, why not?"

"If history couldn't do it, and still can't, why you?"

"Oh, all right, because I'm God," I said sulkily.

"I'll come up and see you after surgery with some good news, so relax and keep your feet dry." And then she went and I was alone again on the battleground.

I glanced at the pearls of wisdom on the walls, took a large wet sponge and cleaned them all off. I could see no possible way of carrying on at that moment. I chalked up instead, "FACE FAILURE AND FIGHT IT".

But the fight was over. The sense of failure wasn't.

16

I began totting up . . . At least Baby had been snouting elsewhere, and only five or six dogs were involved instead of the dozen in the house. At least none of them were badly hurt and neither was I. At least now I could watch out for trouble. At least I knew who created it and where he would have to go, and at least the summer was nearly over. But, if the summer was nearly over, what next?

When the phone rang, I went to it prepared to accept possibly my last customer. It was my husband. The eye of the storm, so to speak.

"Just been told I can leave," he said.

"Wonderful," I said without much enthusiasm.

"So I'm going down to do some fishing with Archie at Newquay," he announced with a trace of defiance.

"Wonderful," I said again, with feeling this time.

"You don't mind?"

"Not if it's what you want to do."

"It is. Right then. That's it. See you sometime." He put down the phone. I knew he was furious I was making no protests. And if I had made any? He'd have possibly been secretly pleased but furious at having to argue to get his own way. And I was furious with myself for getting less upset than I had over the dog-fight. It did rather seem as if I was the fall guy for everything happening.

By the time Hetty arrived I was eating marzipan, the ultimate anti-depressive.

"Put it down," said Hetty, "you'll get fat and ugly . . ."

"So who'll care?" I asked gloomily. I told her about Pa's fishing trip. Then I wailed, "No one ever sees me: I never see anyone. I want to go and be a wet fishmonger somewhere like the middle of a supermarket where dogs aren't permitted. I'm giving up."

"Oh no, you're not. You're just beginning. You're a Canine Psycho-analyst. Your first patient is on his way in. Your fees are astronomical and in future you can forget boarding and concentrate on one or two urgent cases at a time."

"Hetty, I have *no* qualifications. Dogs fight when they get near me now. I get panicky. I nearly used Worcester Sauce instead of Friar's Balsam. I'm weak-willed. I give in under pressure. And what's more, I don't know anything."

"But you make a nice consommé from pigs' trotters," she said. "Oh, come on, you get on with dogs. You've got a way with them."

"I'd never get away with setting myself up as a canine Fred!"

"Freud."

"Fred Freud, then. Great jeers would go up amongst all my friends."

"It's not your friends we're interested in."

Had I any friends? I could count two or three, but where had they been when I needed them?

At least I had nothing to lose. "OK," I sighed, "wheel him in."

I had to be realistic. There was still Hetty's bill. She kept shrugging it off. She would say, "Maybe you can do something for me sometime." It would have to be something pretty terrific, but maybe this was the start of it. So I followed her out, still making token protests.

"I can't take your patients. I'd get struck off!"

"You're not on," she said witheringly, "and I'm not talking about tumours or renal failures or anal glands. Of course not. But I do get a lot of psychosomatic cases. Don't laugh!" She spoke so sharply I stopped at once. "It can be pretty sad. Usually dogs. Cats don't suffer that way. They have a survival structure of their own. A sort of withdrawal system. I'm not sure about hamsters and budgies. But dogs suffer like we do – from loneliness, over-protection, inability to adapt to changed environment and circumstances. Being so domesticated they get bewildered by their lack of complete understanding. Aggression as a defence only brings further punishment which makes it all worse. Things like over-feeding mean indigestion and bad temper, just like anybody's Grandad. I can give pills to relax taut nerves and stress, but it's usually the owners who need help. I can give advice and diet sheets because I can often see the exact problem, but I can't enforce the treatment, and twenty minutes in the Surgery can't be good news for bad vibes and mental suffering." She suddenly looked perplexed, at a loss. It was incomprehensible in Hetty. "I've always wanted these emotional sufferers to just *be* for a while, under supervision by someone sensitive enough to *see* and perhaps understand, sympathise, help." She shrugged. "During their time with you, I could call in and we could discuss symptoms and progress, much as humans benefit from a psychiatric unit with a visiting consultant. In any case, just getting away from their owners for a short time helps re-establish identity."

Today the Canine Butlins, I thought: tomorrow the Nobel Prize for – well – something. I might yet qualify for a place among the all-time Greats. A panorama of success began, as usual, to unroll before my eyes.

But I still had a few doubts. "Oh, Hetty!" I squeaked, "I can't cope with canine hysteria!"

"What is it you've been doing for the past few months, then?"

Bustle's cuddles, Rover's insecurity, Teddy's prayers. Then there was the alsatian, Ruthless. Trembling, he had leapt into the branches of the apple tree as I stood talking to the owner while beneath, waving her tail in triumph and spitting cynical whiskers, Frilly had stalked up and down daring it to drop.

I had, of course, apologised. "She's only a few months old and she's never done this before, though she is a bit bossy, I know." I picked Frilly up and scolded her lovingly.

The dog had put out an appealing paw and whimpered. The owner said glumly, "I'm afraid he's always like this with cats. I'm ashamed every time it happens, though he's never gone up a tree before. I've tried everything – getting him a kitten of his own, lining his basket with a Pussypillow, thumping him."

Hadn't I used a sixth sense then? Some might have called it a Pseud's psychiatrick, of course, but I protested, "You can't instil confidence with violence. Don't you see? It's become a phobia now, like spiders." (That was one I knew I would never conquer.) "He associates cats and kittens with your deepest emotions because you react so strongly. It worries him. He's scared up a tree at the threat of losing your love to a kitten. An ex-police dog you said? I expect he was taught not to chase cats, anyway, and it's all gone too far."

Maybe it hadn't been one of my clearer reasonings but the owner admitted a trifle bitterly, "They never told us why they had to find such a young dog a good home and I didn't ask – well, you don't, do you?" I would have done, but it was a bit late to say so, and he'd gone on, "Early retirement, they said. But of course, trained like that you expect Fearless Obedience. We never thought he'd be a she. That's why we called him Ruthless you see."

And I'd seen. Ruthless had been sitting so awkwardly in the tree it was obvious. The man had said they really wanted a dog. "A *dog*, not a lady one." For many people, the word "bitch" is only used when referring to humans. "Well, then they offered us one and we never thought of checking till after. But you don't expect lady dogs to tackle criminals, do you?" His naïvety had been touching. "And she looks like a dog, doesn't she? I mean, like a *dog*. And we were desperate for a guard dog – the wife's got some nice bits and bobs after all – so we took him on and then found his name was Ruth and he was a she . . ." I had to sympathise. A man likes his women feminine, his car fast, his dog virile and all three to do as they're told, thus establishing his own identity.

I took Ruthless willingly because I recognised my kind of mentality so well – scared to death of a spider yet eager to rush in where angels fear to tread. We all look into a distorting mirror when we choose a pet and seeing ourselves there provokes nothing but exasperation after the initial delight.

Ruthless had taken his chance and found his level along with the rest. It was then I realised that communal coping did a great deal more for the average problem pet than any veterinary shrink couch. Self-survival is the great healer, and his master, after a backward glance of disappointment at Ruthless, nodded with relief and went back to his red car, pallid wife and Cornish holiday, leaving the final problem with me to sort out.

I think he felt a sense of failure, and maybe guilt. Most owners suffer from conscience at depriving a faithful friend of their company, favourite chair and the boredom of a walk to the pub every evening. But in all the cases I handled, old Chummy was happy enough after the first twenty-four hours. Given a bone, a ball and a blonde bitch picked up in the Exercise Yard, and he was probably running neck and neck with his master in the Holiday Stakes anyhow.

Ruthless had accepted help down from the tree, snuffled gratefully into my hand, licked and jumped around with relief. It finally confirmed the gender. A dog would have enjoyed a good shake, wagged his tail in triumph and swaggered off as if he'd won a particularly glorious battle. His owner had mentioned the shame he felt when Ruthless failed to cock his leg in public. "A *squatting* alsatian!" he had said with humility. "It looks ridiculous!" Poor Ruthless always glanced at me uneasily when about to relieve herself.

It must have been very difficult for Ruthless who never seemed quite sure what sex prevailed. In the end, after a lot of consideration, I remembered the phrase "a gay dog", decided Ruthless was one of them, and left it at that . . .

And as soon as the pressure was off and we all knew where we were, there was no more trouble. Ruthless integrated (because she had to, however uneasily) and though she shied away from Frilly for a few days, she watched carefully and found the little cat offered no threat, either physical or emotional, and ended ignoring her almost completely. By the time Ruthless was collected, she was boisterous, confident, almost harmlessly aggressive. I thought she was even going to cock her leg before she got in the car.

I recounted the entire incident to Hetty with some pride. I felt it would confirm my ability and her faith in my specialised insight. I also told her she was wrong about cats having their own survival structure because we had a Siamese once who leapt in a pan of frying bacon, lapped curry powder with relish and preferred tea-towels to fish-heads at lunchtime. It would only sleep in a closed drawer and had to be shut in every night, leaving me to sneak down in the early hours to make sure it wasn't suffocated. I went on to say that if, later, I happened to be called in at Buckingham Palace to cope with corgi problems, I might try and persuade Her Majesty to have Yorkshire terriers instead.

"Fun things, Hetty, I know. But don't you see, it would save wear and tear on the staff and our defence programme. All those chewed-up sentries, and anyway it's a case of nationalities, so I'm sure . . ." but Hetty yawned and said, "You do get carried away, don't you? Ben's yelling his head off about something . . ."

Ben shouted, "Someone's been sick on the rug in the hall!" and I descended to earth with a floor cloth.

Hetty watched me. She said, "I need them to live domestically. Normal household routine." I raised my eyebrows. "Nothing special." I laughed a hollow laugh. Nothing was special at this particular Health Farm. It was more like a boarding-house at Skeggie. "Just the relaxed atmosphere you've created." I swung my bucket with an air of utter abandon to careless rapture.

When the rug was airing off outside, I went back and found Ben telling Hetty about his recordings. "It's odd when you think about it. They've had centuries to pick up at least a smattering of language, so you'd think they could, at least, ask the time. I was only in France with the school for ten days and I could say 'Piss off' and 'Where's the loo' in French within twenty-four hours!" If that's all he learned, it seemed the dogs had a point in not bothering. They don't need to tell the time anyway. They leave all that to us. I began to see there was a lot more in dogs than barks and bones.

The rug was no end improved by the scrub. I remembered a friend who told me she always encouraged her puppy to pee in different places on the carpet, not just to be sure of an overall effect, but to get the entire thing shampooed in the time it took to complete house-training. With a litter you could cover a whole mansion.

"I shall study my findings anyway," said Ben importantly. "But a lot needs explaining. When people arrive, do they bark a welcome or a threat? or both? or one at a time? and if so who gets what and why?" I said most callers don't bark at all.

But he didn't appreciate flippancy just then, so Hetty and I went back to her car where my first inmate was waiting. Hetty said, "Ben's a bit of all right, isn't he?" She sounded amused. "What's that dog following him?"

"Pathos – the border collie. He's lovely. The owner called him

Pathos because he thought it was the name of one of the Three Musketeers. He only discovered ages later it was Porthos. Still, it suits him. He was snatched from the gas chamber in a Dogs' Refuge (refuge?) just as his time was up, like a Dumas melodrama. He needs someone for security all the time and he chose Ben. Ben likes him, too. He sleeps in his room." I meant the dog slept in Ben's room, but in this house it amounted to the same thing.

I don't know what I expected to be in the car when at last we got round to introductions. Certainly not a chihuahua in a workbasket. A limp borzoi with anguished eyes perhaps, or a sad labrador. Not the sharp-eared, bug-eyed baby monster weighing me up and finding me short on expectations.

"Not much the matter there," I pronounced with confidence. I reached out a hand to stroke the silky head and soften those glaring eyes. Within seconds I was sucking a socking great tear in my finger, made by a set of tiny evil little teeth.

"I should have warned you to watch it," murmured Hetty smugly. "*That's* the problem!" The dog was licking his lips as if he'd just had a foretaste of Chef's Special.

"He'll be your Test Case," said Hetty, trying not to guffaw, "and if you can stop him nipping everyone in sight, I'll believe you can do anything."

I said, "So I can walk on water, too. He may be the size of a grasshopper but he's got a mind like a chutney tomato, sharp and acid. Pippy, with it . . ."

"The owners are desperate. I've told them all about you. I've said you have this fantastic rapport with dogs and they're going to be *so* grateful! They actually love the little beast and he's worth pots of money. Well up to show standard, this one." You could just see him sitting in a silver cup, taking the fingers off the judges.

"Right," I said busily, wearing my professional hat, "let's get down to details. Owners' name?" Hetty, wearing gloves, held the basket at arms' length. It was satin-lined, pink, with quilting. I had notebook out, pen poised.

"No names. Sorry. They're a bit touchy about it. Seems someone threatened proceedings after losing a leg in passing. Now they're scared their defence will be ruined if they have to admit he's in for treatment. You come under Boarding, so it's OK so long as no one finds out more than that." She could rely on our complete discretion, Madam.

"Background then?"

"Young couple, wealthy home, out a lot. Dog left with cleaners and au pairs. Only they can't get cleaners and au pairs any more since he started this lark."

"Insecure," I concluded, putting my pen away as if the problem were now solved.

"Sure he is," agreed Hetty. "Who isn't? But what do you do about it?" She got up to go.

I shouted, "Hey! what's his name?"

"Jumbo," she said, "Jet for short." She was off to the W.I. She said her talk was to be on "Wool-Gathering" though one look at her own sleek couture clothes would have put one off knitting for life.

Jumbo bared his fangs at me the minute I tried to move his work-basket. He looked like the Littlest Dragon diminished by one wave of the Magic Wand. I wish they'd tried two. It might have completed the job.

Ben was on his knees trying to get the amiable Pudding to beg. She fell over every time but went on obliging. "She'd be OK if her back legs were fatter," Ben commented, and I realised for the first time that you can't tell much about what goes on under a thick curly coat.

I said, "This is Jumbo. He bites."

"Not among this lot he won't. Not if he knows what's good for him," Ben said grimly.

I looked round and saw the wary eyes weighing up the situation. They could sense trouble quicker than I could now. I put down the workbasket again and sent the others out for Compulsory Games, as Ben called it. He said it was just like school – come hell or high rainwater and Wednesday afternoons saw them all outside kicking or batting a ball about while the staff indulged with relief some games of their own, out of sight. I urged Jumbo out of his basket with a wooden spoon. He looked like a plastic toy. Tiny, detailed and breakable. If his head had been shrunk any further he would have had a pea brain. What on earth led me to believe he hadn't? Couldn't he see there was no threat from anyone?

Ben was asking about the evening meal. During the day we each ate what, where and when we wanted, but the evening called for a more sociable approach and until a day or two earlier I had always cooked a proper sit-down, slap-up knife and fork affair. Then a few nights before, while watching me, Ben said he thought he'd like to try his hand, and the next night he'd take over. I was only too willing. I left him to it and was amazed at the meal he managed, even if it was nearly ten o'clock by the time it was ready. Flushed with success and wine-tasting for the Coq au Vin, Ben offered to be responsible for the cooking from then on – or until he grew tired of the job which would be as soon as the novelty wore off, I presumed. But who looks a gift horse in the mouth when it's full of hay?

Going through a carton of cookery books, Ben had found several on other subjects, one of them boldly entitled *Your Dog (Its Breeding & Character)*. I found it again – lurking in the vegetable rack. I sat on the floor and turned up CHIHUAHUA.

The illustration at least confirmed Jumbo's origins. South American ladies, I read, carried the tiny dog under one arm, facing backwards, so that gentlemen making unwelcome advances from behind got pretty sharply nipped in the bud – or somewhere even more painful. This seemed pertinent to the present problem. It also proved a theory that dogs bred for specific purposes in times past, never quite lose the instinct to react for that purpose, whatever their surroundings. So that working dogs like to work even in this day and age of leisure. And dogs bred for attack can hardly be blamed if they do just that when the man from next door drops in to borrow a bottle-opener. And even joke dogs, like Jumbo, remember, from deep down, some intuition to nip, however indiscriminately.

The only trouble was that the writer gave not the slightest hint on how to divert the impulse towards more peaceful ends.

I had another look through the carton. Mrs Beeton and The Galloping Gourmet rubbed uneasy spines together. A very old copy of *Jack's Reference Book*, somebody's pale parent of the more recent *Enquire Within*, emerged with a leaflet entitled *Spavins & Windgalls*. For one awful moment, I was taken back to the days I almost spent as an unsuccessful fruit-grower, but it went on to advise Squills for Carriage Horses and I saw the date was 1904. Then up came Dr Foster. His attack was robust, his cures drastic. But on the few occasions in the past when I tried any, the effects had been astounding. I turned to Chapter 5 DOGS and then to a section headed *Breeds*. Each breed had a sub-section under "Complaints Common" with Causes and Cures, Physical and – amazingly – Emotional. Dr Foster must have been very much ahead of his time to even consider dogs *could* have emotions.

I couldn't believe my luck. Here was my salvation, the foundation of my eventual success as an Animal Analyst. I settled back with confidence and relief.

He presented his cures from actual cases. Under "Emotional" he began: "A gentleman of my acquaintance referred me to his extremely vicious hound, a strange breed mixture of Elk and Pointer and requested I use my knowledge and experience to bring the dog to reason. I suggested I take the creature to my home for a few days for close observation and eventual treatment" (hey! wasn't *I* the first Canine Shrink?) "and fortunately, even with relief I may say, he agreed."

I caught the words "complete success" at the bottom of the page, which was full of small close print, and decided it was too detailed and important to be read whilst sitting on the floor by an old carton marked Lux Liquid. I took the book with me to the downstairs cloakroom where comparative peace is generous to concentration. I don't go much for loos which resemble small ante-rooms to a boudoir in the style of the French Empire; nor do I care for the attempt at an atmosphere of Fun Place in a Sun Club somewhere towards Majorca. Time will be when the trendy loo turns from tasselled handles, potted palms and porn, and be shown in colour pages as simple, tiled in white, functional and beautifully uncomplicated. Then we can all find somewhere to think. I was already into the trad. lav. line. There is nothing so new as a prototype.

Dr Foster, abbreviated, believed a dog's life was similar to that of a foreigner, unable to understand culture and manners and language of a native race. Some foreigners picked it all up quickly and easily. Others took longer, but managed to fumble their way through, and a few never really did get the hang of things, remained bewildered by it all and became arrogant to the point of defiance in despair, finally reverting back to their origins as a method of self-defence.

He went on, in the Treatment bit, to say it was no good beating the dog about the ears to get some sort of unwilling submission. He said he himself used to appeal to the dog's better nature by inviting sympathy.

I read on with growing fascination. Somewhere the phone rang. I left it to Ben. How had Dr Foster done it? I saw him in his immaculate Edwardian frock coat and beaver hat on all fours, whining and wingeing. But that wasn't quite what he meant. "Make sure the dog knows you're his friend and that you like him," he advised – adding without cynicism, "even if you don't. That you're not going to bite *him*." (Easy that one: he'd be in there first anyway.) "Be sad when he attacks you" (even easier) "and whatever you do, *let him see* your distress. Make a performance of crying, wring your hands, throw yourself about in a state of hysterical anguish. Dogs have deeply compassionate natures. Once you have won his sympathy he will become your defender, your champion, not your attacker."

I was enchanted. The approach hardly ranked with standard psychiatry but it had a kind of underlying common-sense I found very appealing. In other words, I could do it. I would be the Sarah Bernhardt of the Surgery Couch. I could hardly wait to get started. I rushed back to the kitchen.

The workbasket was empty. Jumbo had gone.

"Ben," I said slowly, "just a minute. Where's the psychiatric case?"

He was whipping up coffee cream to line a sandwich sponge. Enough to fill the Sydney Harbour. He barely raised his eyes.

"Probably behind an earwig or under an egg cup?"

He could be very annoying. I had to find Jumbo before Hetty came in on her way back from the W.I. and en route to the Jersey Herd she was currently visiting. The owner was an absent pop star who bought farm, herd, house, machinery and even the resident manager and staff out of the proceeds from baring his hairy chest, cracking his pelvic bones and hollering down a jug. But it was a lovely sound on Radio 1 where you couldn't see it and gave one a personal share in decadence without the trouble of having to actually disintegrate oneself. That's why pop stars deserve their wealth. They're the whipping-boys for the rest of us in a mainly mild society. They take our scourges, wear our hair shirts, and they provide the satisfaction of debauchery second-hand. The farm, Hetty said, was immaculate, money being no object to organisation and animal welfare. His employees were well paid and happy, the output to the community excellent. So what if the owner was headlined at pop concerts and in the press as Farmer (Hips) Harry with the impression he spent most of his time in the milking-sheds? Or on a tractor wearing overalls in pouring rain? Politicians do it, too. Farmers themselves now sit in leather-lined offices with computers instead of cows.

I scrambled down on my hands and knees and peered under the sink cupboard, the lower chairs, the cleaning cupboard, fridge and behind the cooker. I even peered fearfully in the dogs' water bowl and beneath Ben's large feet. I got up again, my mouth dry with dread. I felt utterly horrified. Bad enough to fail with my first case, but to *lose* it . . .

Ben took the sponge cake, cooling on a rack by the window, and began spreading coffee cream. He said, somewhere aside of his concentration, "You could try the flower-pots." On the window-sill were a row of geraniums I kept forgetting to water. As they showed signs of protest, I would hurriedly offer a complete drench with apologies and put them on the floor by the back door in the shade for a few days. Some of these pots were empty, like vacated beds in a geriatric ward, their contents having been returned to the good earth outside. Jumbo was in one of them, like a pop-eyed pot plant, staring defiantly at me. Very still. I put my hand out to soothe the sharp little ears – and withdrew it hastily as it met the chattering teeth.

I got up and mopped my eyes, licked my finger and stamped my feet.

"I'm not so sure about this new profession," I said furiously. "I'll have to demand danger money. I'll need compensation and a guarantee of financial protection at the very least. I wonder how I stand regarding Insurance? I must enquire how much I get for the loss of a finger. But it might be best to quit the game altogether while I'm still more or less complete." My finger was bleeding vigorously.

Ben put the sponge in the fridge. He put everything in the fridge or the oven. Ben's food was all red hot or frozen. He turned, satisfied, and said with eyebrows away, "What, *you*? Give in? Admit you can't cope with a mock-up mouse?"

I remembered that the other dogs loved chocolate biscuits. I never did meet a dog who couldn't be coaxed with cocoa in some form or other. I often used it for pill-administration, powdered pill mixing in without detection on a plate. I broke off a bit of a chocolate wholemeal and held it out to the pot on a wooden spoon, making soothing noises. I could have used my hand in a glove, but the smell of a glove would have been deceiving, and anything as alert as Jumbo would lose any faith glimmering way back there to be dug out. The crumb was pondered for a long time and then grabbed. Right, I thought, I'm one paw ahead. Let's keep it that way. After all, once you trust Greeks bearing gifts you may as well ask them to tea. I went back to the table and fetched the packet. I had plenty of time ahead of me.

When had I thought to myself, once before, long ago, that there had to be a less ridiculous way to make money? But it wasn't too bad sitting there, on the floor in the sunshine from the long windows, dishing out crumbs to a flea in a flower-pot. I knew I was using physical persuasion rather than psychological cunning, but I was, after all, working on a very physically activated case, with a lot of the old primitive instincts left – albeit in some confusion but definitely intact.

Above me, where I'd begun again on the chalked reminders, a recent one read "CONSTANT WASHING WEARS AWAY A STONE". This little homily can be taken two ways if it is to be taken at all. On the one hand it can come as a comfort when the hot water is low in the tank or the boiler's gone out, and on the other hand could be taken as an urge to have a good scrub at anything in need when I was feeling too lazy to bother. The fact that its effects were so diametrically opposed usually meant it resulted in nothing at all, but now I took heart from a third possibility and persevered. *Patience*, I hoped, *would have its own reward.*

After a little while I gave up the spoon and went back to finger-risking. A quick nip was enough – for Jumbo. Definitely not to be compared with chocolate wholemeal. Ben was upstairs, taping Clover, a scottie with asthma. I kept pointing out the noises she made were symptomatic of her complaint rather than emotion, but Ben said he needed all the material he could get and one gruff snuffle was as good as another. It seemed I had an ideal opportunity to put into practice Dr Foster's invaluable advice.

Jumbo was now at the point of taking biscuit from my fingers. I was recognised. Accepted, in fact. My soothing words grew more and more plaintive. I had to catch his sympathy before he got fed up with biscuit. I creased my face into an expression of acute suffering, tried first a deep sob, a long-drawn-out gulp and sniff. Not very compelling, but rather like being behind the scenes on the dress rehearsal night for a RADA Finals. Or later, perhaps, when the results come through?

The ears twitched, the nose twiddled. The little head was jerked to one side. Encouraged by my talent, I threw myself into the roles of tragedy and despair.

"Jumbo! Jumbo!" I cried, in the sort of voice I use when somebody drops the gravy boat, "you're breaking my heart, tormenting my soul! Why do you do this to me, Jumbo!" I stifled a giggle. He would, I knew, suspect the very smallest hint of insincerity. I tried to think of something solemn. Something to make me really cry. As my family say, I'm the only tele-viewer ever to be moved to anguish by commercials for scouring powder. It was infuriating that I could barely raise a tear when faced with the necessity now. Anything too awful, I couldn't even let myself contemplate. Suddenly it seemed I had simply nothing to cry about. Surely, I thought desperately, surely there's something disappointing in my life?

There were one or two outstanding accounts from slow-paying customers, but I long ago learnt how to deal with these. If they were reluctant to pay on collection I sent two accounts and then a statement for double the original amount. I would get a letter back by return, with a cheque, saying *this* was the figure agreed and *this* was all they were settling for and, etc. etc. I rather grudged the stamp on my letter of apology that followed, but it usually brought them back again when I was needed.

Poetry makes me cry. I tried a few lines from *One Of Us Two* – and if the very idea of Ella Wheeler Wilcox makes you laugh I suggest you read that. But it was too much. I tried to put it out of my head and went back to hamming up a dramatic monologue.

"What have you done to me, Jumbo? What terrible thing have you done?" (What, indeed?) "I am dying of love, unrequited: and that's not my idea of fun!" I ruined the whole thing by laughing. I didn't mean it to rhyme but when you've been at it for long, these kind of treatments often develop hysteria – not only in the patient, either.

I pulled myself together. Jumbo was looking positively shocked. It was hardly the reaction I wanted. I began again. This time in real earnest.

"Oh, Jumbo! Jumbo!" I yawned as I went on "Oooh! Jumbo. What will become of us? Help me! save me! do not desert me, Jumbo!" I raised my voice in a quivering crescendo of cries. "Have pity on me, Jumbo!" Tears were pouring down my cheeks from one yawn after another, caught up in the cascade of sobs. I leant back against the table leg, shifting a little on the hard floor, and dragging the cloth with my shoulder. A cup of cold coffee, balanced precariously near the edge, slid off and the brown liquid trickled down my shirt, but I was watching Jumbo from the corner of my eye and could detect a distinct response – interest, followed by concern. I was delighted. A few more sobs and we would be home and, er, dry? Well, success would have crowned Dr Foster's advice, anyhow. I revved myself up for a few final efforts while I tried to ignore the cold coffee drips down my cleavage. "I love you, I love you, Fernando!" I cried wildly, plaintively, giving impetus to any Thespian qualities I might have. It was nothing Henrik Ibsen would have applauded, nor anything Laurence Olivier would have attempted, but it appealed to the patient. I was almost banging my head on the table in despair as I sobbed, "All that is left is death and dishonour!" and I let out a wail of despair.

Ben, suddenly behind me, said, "I don't think so, Mr Shane. She's not usually like this. If you care to wait a little . . ."

I shot to my feet, dripping tears and cold coffee. A tall man was standing in the doorway, Angel on his shoulder, Toby at his side. Toby, looked as if he'd won the Treble Chance in marrow bones.

I dusted down my jeans and held out a chewed, crummy and thoroughly mucky hand. "How do you do," I said, awkwardly. "I do beg your pardon. I didn't hear you come in. You must excuse me." He was looking more amused than offended. I put on a voice of professional dignity. "I've been trying to win through to a disturbed patient. The Dr Foster Emotional Approach, you know." And then, because I could see he was wiping his hand down Toby's coat, "Together with biscuits . . ."

In the end we all sat down at the table and had tea. The sponge cake was a bit leaden in parts, but Mr R. Shane said how good it was to be back in Britain, with afternoon tea, where you never knew just what to expect, and he laughed. But I think he meant my scene with Jumbo. I asked where he'd been and he said in Europe, for an oil change. I wasn't really sure what he meant, so smiled politely and said I hoped he was OK now, and he said he felt a lot better.

"But how," I asked him, "did you come to leave Toby and Angel on our doorstep?" I tried to sound very stern and disapproving, but he was such a nice friendly man it wasn't easy. He made no apologies, anyway.

"Mrs Sissingtons," he said, unashamedly feeding his sponge cake to Toby.

"Who?"

"Mrs Sissingtons – you know, the Port-in-a-Storm Agency? Will undertake to do anything at any time? Advertises in the evening papers?"

"No." I didn't get any evening papers. Mrs Sissingtons was a stranger without. I wasn't sure how she became involved within.

"I rang them: said I had to leave dog and cat somewhere in a rush as my sister, who always has them if I have to go away, was on holiday. Mrs Sissingtons was wonderful. She'll undertake anything you can't do yourself." This conjured up innumerable problems of my own. The name was worth remembering.

"For a fee, of course."

The name could be forgotten. Hope died.

"Such as an air ticket to Khatmandu in half an hour, say, or the one place left where you can study a blue-eyed ginger rattlesnake in its habitat. Even someone to sort out your knitting, tax claims, or one of those recipes suggested by the late chef of some eastern mandarin. She found me the location of a banyan tree in Brazil once." ("My shirt's made of that," chipped in Ben. "That's Banlon!" I hissed. "Do go on, Mr Shane.") "And she'll find a place for your kids to stay while you run off with a friend, or take over all responsibilities while you emigrate with a lover" (I would remember her name after all) "or your dog and cat when you're needing an oil change."

"Amazing," I said, inadequately. He said she had found us almost at once. I wasn't sure whether to be flattered.

"I don't know her," I said suspiciously. "How does she know us?"

"Local papers," he said. "She gets them all, has a team scanning small ads. An excellent filing system. Studies her field, checks, recommends, always has a second string ready." Angel was lapping milk from his teaspoon.

And she'd chosen me! "I wonder who our second string was?" I mused. Nice to be first, like a fiddle in a Philharmonic. I always said I would make it this time.

"You were second to the Wagatail Corner Kennels actually. They were full. Not that I'd go any old where. Most of them make hay in summer." It seemed a funny reason for turning them down. "I mean they take far too many during the season; Fleas, too."

"Fleas?" I repeated, mystified. "People board *fleas*?"

"Well, yes, you could say that. On dogs and monkeys and cats and things. They spread like wildfire." I remembered the leaping gymnasts we found on Toby but tact is my middle name, specially with paying guests.

"How awful!" I said, more shocked at my own hypocrisy than anything. I spent most of my time with what Ben referred to as the Deflouser. Whatever they brought with them in their coats, I made sure they went home without. The final check was like frisking visitors for teaspoons.

When I glanced round, Jumbo had crept out of his flower-pot, the pointed ears like brittle autumn leaves. I pretended not to notice, but I put a bit of sponge on one finger and dropped my hand low beneath the table, offering it courageously. Jumbo hesitated and then took a quick lick. I jumped as I felt his tongue and Mr Shane looked puzzled, but Jumbo let me go unbitten and I brought back my hand into view and smiled, my head reeling with success.

"Hurrah!" I said quietly. "I've cracked it!" but at the same moment something like a fullstop leapt across the cloth and I shot out a hand to drop the sugar bowl on it, sending the sugar all over Jumbo and the floor beneath.

I discovered later it was a thunder-bug.

I was only minimally sorry when Mr Shane, Angel and Toby had gone. I knew I would sadly miss Toby, even though his great tail would no longer sweep clear every low table and shelf in the house, and his tongue no longer pant in my ear.

Mr R. Shane told us, before he left, that Toby had fished the Angel out of a river in Scotland, when they had been staying up there. "Salmon, we wanted," he said with a laugh, "but old Tobe here has to find a kitten – a few weeks old. We don't know if it fell in or was thrown. Toby's like that though, always pushing his nose in and coming up with something. This time he had to be responsible for what he got but he managed somehow, although he often nearly drowned her again in saucers of milk. That's why they're so devoted, of course."

They left in a large car, leaving a cheque for twice the normal fees, not because I took advantage of his good nature, but R. Shane said he wanted to be sure we would have them back again if necessary.

I never did find out about the oil change.

Jumbo got back in the flower-pot after they'd gone and sat there glowering for the rest of the evening. I would have to start all over again the next day, but for that night I put his workbasket in the bedroom cupboard where he would feel close to the rest of us, even if it meant nothing to him. I was quite flattered when he clung to the sides of the basket with tiny claws and made no attempt to nip me.

Ben didn't like Jumbo much. The regard was mutual, though. There was no particular animosity, they just ignored one another. Jumbo stayed in his flower-pot by day, apart from exercise in Shelmerdine's playpen, left behind on collection as his own part of the garden was well walled in at home. I wired it round with chicken mesh, or Jumbo would have been off like a jet.

Dr Foster must have known a thing or two because after a couple of days sobbing and pleading and appealing to his better nature, Jumbo actually gave in. Ben said even the Kray Twins would have taken religious orders to shut me up. After Jumbo had taken the easy way out and began to integrate, he actually developed a passion for silly Tilly, a bedlington with a back like the Loch Ness monster and a pair of flattened leathery ears. Tilly was never still, and about as bright as a 15 watt bulb. But she was a ball of fun and quite fascinated Jumbo. They played ceaselessly and upset Mattie and one or two of the rest. Jumbo copped a clip round the ear a few times from one or other of the older dogs and I felt my heart stop beating when I realised one bite would finish him off.

But he survived and the very challenge of holding his own in a canine community made individual idiosyncracies impossible. He was hustled, intrigued, curious, entertained, amused and far too wary to adopt any of his former aggression.

At the weekend, several of the boarders were collected and only one came in. I was relieved and dismayed at the same time, but when Hetty came by and saw the reformed Jumbo, she was so thrilled she promised a queue of desperate patients for my remedial clinic as soon as I could accept them. I suggested that Jumbo's owners should treat him as a proper dog and not as a cuddly puppy, and that they should consider letting him have a companion. I think half the trouble was he wanted to be seen as a dog, in spite of being tiny. Like any short politician, he saw his power being diminished by his size and only by asserting himself in any way he could, was he able to find any confidence.

Oh, well, that was my explanation. Ben said it was the clip round the ear Jumbo got when he had a go at Ben's fingers. Maybe if you're small you get away with things more easily and get top-heavy about rights and privileges.

I told Marsha. I suppose I must have been excited by my achievement because I actually rang her to say so. I rushed straight into it all and gave a blow by blow account from start to finish, ending up in a complete run-down of everybody's praise and casually mentioning the enormous cheque which completed it.

Marsha said "Good-oh!" and then mentioned that she met the trumpeter N. E. Price at the S.S. and they took a weekend away in the West Country. And wasn't it odd? She'd seen my husband there. He looked fantastic! Very tanned and well.

"You don't have a thing to worry about, darling! He seems very very happy and wonderfully looked after. He said to tell you he'd be OK." She was only *just* gloating.

And me? He hadn't written for a week and only rung once since the weekend because he said it was so difficult on someone else's phone bill. When I rang him, he was always out and I got second-hand messages from the housekeeper.

It ruined my moment of glory. I said "That's terrific. Must go. I've someone waiting," in a lowered voice which made it sound like a wild clandestine affair, conducted passionately in a kennel. It was easier to ring my husband, and be bitchy.

Pa was in. He said "Marsha? Oh, Lor' yes, I saw Marsha! Unfortunately she saw me first! Why? What did she say?"

"It wasn't what she said but what she made clear she wasn't *going* to say that made me uncomfortable."

"Like what?"

"It's not worth bothering about," loftily: why had I gained the impression he was with someone like Angharad Rees, barefoot and beautiful on Cornish cliffs?

"I never could stand that woman. She came out of the mos expensive hotel with some feller in crotch-clutchers and a bald head about half her size."

I felt a bit better, but only marginally. Later, I wondered why cared so much. And even if I did. I began to wonder exactly who h was because it had been so long since I saw him, and so much ha happened to us both. Incarcerated in one place for a whole summer alone and unable to leave, I, at least, had become a different person I wasn't sure how different, but definitely not the same. He ha been close to death, recovered, lost his responsibilities for a time, had been able to relax and shed skins of the usual anxieties in daily living, and we stood on separate islands with a wide channel running deep between.

Physical distance is nothing to the damage of an emotional breach. We both knew it had grown up over the months. Me, rightly or wrongly, from a resentment he could hardly realise when he, on his side, was probably only aware of the same thing against my apparent desertion. I could see no way at all of bridging the gap easily. I wasn't even sure I wanted to.

I told Hetty. She said, "It may be better that way," and shocked me into silence because, as usual, she was right. Getting together against any real wish from either of us could only lead to trouble. Apart we were, at least, quite happy. Why risk it?

"Anyway," said Hetty, "forget it. Your next Case is on its way," and she put down the phone. Hetty's husband, Mike, was hardly ever mentioned. He travelled all over the world. He constructed bridges, viaducts and motorways which kept him abroad for months at a time. So maybe Hetty knew how I felt.

She was always being proved right.

I7

"This is Smudge," announced Hetty. "Or Fudge . . ." She paused. "No, I'm sure it's Smudge." She held up a small bundle of scruffy white fur. She said "A very sickly Smudge, actually."

I took him in my arms, and was shocked. He was almost weightless.

Smudge was at least a new name. Tiggys and Mitzis and Susies came and went, taking the place of the Lassies and Rovers and Princes of my own childhood. It proved only that Females have caught up at last, and not only in the human world. Bitches were more popular than dogs. Bitches Are Best. It took a long time for this tc be realised but now, taking hold, proving it true, there's a great deal more hope for the future.

Hetty will never quite forget the Smudge episode. Neither will I And neither, I feel sure, will Smudge. But the day he arrived, I gav up before even asking what was wrong. He seemed beyond humar aid, let alone mine.

"He's wasting away!" I cried, with the anguish of a Victoria heroine. Hetty leant against the table. Her hair had grown since w first met and was now curling round her shoulders instead of he ears. She wore tussore culottes with matching mushroom-coloure suede boots and tee shirt. She would have made any double-pag spread for *Penthouse* into a star issue. I glanced at my own hai as I passed the mirror. It looked like a demented broom in compari son, but then so did some of the nicest dogs I knew. Together w could always contribute towards the *Hardware Weekly*.

Hetty took the mug with SIP ME QUICK on it and stroked the ne patient's head. "Poor little thing . . . he belongs to a nice middl aged couple who think the world of him. He's a first cross Maltes probably Lhasa Apso. Four or five years old. Healthy apart from few minor things until now. I mean the usual sore-paw or queer-e and that sort of thing." I waited. She added sugar to the coffee. N calories ever erupted round Hetty's hips.

"But he's not eating now?" I said, stating the obvious. Of cours a lot of dogs go off their food from time to time. Not a bad thin really. They act on instinct where their health matters, as well other things, and it might do most of us a lot of good to be the sam Slows down traffic on one's inner Spaghetti Junction. "Is that all?"

"Since ten days ago?"

He had that limp, listless lack of resistance which goes with re illness. I felt ribs sticking out, saw saliva from the slack jaw, the lifeless eyes, felt not just shock and horror, but an awful dread. I was their last hope and if there was nothing *I* could do, this dear, little, sad, pathetic scrap would starve to death.

"Anorexia Nervosa?" I suggested nervously, covering the way I felt with a grim joke.

"I've checked everything internally. No temperature, blockage or intestinal trouble. Nothing to show why he won't eat and they've tried everything, too. I've had to come to the conclusion it's psychosomatic." I made a note of the splendid word, definitely to be used in my first paper for the Veterinary Society, together with "gallimaufrey" and "gallinaceous" which I always feel I can eventually work in somewhere once I know exactly what they mean.

"Hetty," I said, "I can't accept such responsibility. I mean if you can't find what's wrong, how on earth can I?"

"Because I think it needs someone who isn't in any way involved. Someone who can see him as he is with a fresh eye." And she added, "If you won't try, there's nothing left."

"Try *what*?" I cried, almost distraught.

"Just try," said Hetty. "I promised them you would. They're putting their final hopes in you," and she left me.

Smudge lay miserably in his basket that first evening, shivering on a thick blanket near a warm fire. I watched him while I fed the rest, hoping he might join in. Fussy dogs often change completely in competition with others and become the first to grab what's going. But Smudge was no fussy eater. He was, suddenly, a non-starter. I made the usual noises about the delights of the minced tongue I offered, an egg beaten in milk, even chocolate. But he merely turned his head away fretfully, his under-jaw loose and leaving a trail of saliva on the dish. His breath was like a blast of fertiliser. Even fresh, cold water merely brought a look of anguish and an eager effort, only to result in him sinking back with pain.

Hetty had said his throat seemed mildly inflamed and dry, but I could see his tongue was a terrible colour. When the rest were settled for the night, I took Smudge to the bathroom where it was warm and quiet and no one would bother us, and nursed him on my knee while trying to weigh up the possible diagnosis. It was easy to think in there, without being nudged by chalked advice or distracted by telephone bells. Ben agreed to hold the fort for an hour. I was determined to find out what was wrong with Smudge before I went to bed, or give up entirely. I really fancied giving up entirely and at once, because I felt that if I didn't do it first, Smudge would have done it by morning. His eyes were half-closed, showing the whites; he panted and his pulse was faint.

Hetty had given injections of glucose or something to keep him going. I was determined to will him not to give in yet. I was sure there was nothing psychologically wrong. A dog might become difficult, noisy, cross, over-emotionally activated, but he doesn't starve himself to death because he's unhappy. We might, but they have more sense. It had to be something he couldn't do much about. Hetty had said, anyway, that his owners had told her his background was stable and secure: that nothing had changed. She also said they told her their marriage was contented and lacking in stress. They even said their sex life was causing no problems. She said she had nodded as if it was a very important point. People watch so much television and get so many ideas about tension and reaction on children, that they are forced to the conclusion that any lack of wild abandon in bed is going to lead at once to delinquency, scurvy and possibly mayhem among the kiddies. I doubt if any improved relationship ever got Jason through his 11 Plus but I daresay a lot of couples enjoyed trying.

I continued to stroke and cuddle Smudge as he lay still, his beard sodden with saliva, and his lower jaw slack. I wiped the wet, desolate eyes. I wished Teddy was there with one of his prayers. I tried a small one myself.

The whole root of the trouble seemed to be in swallowing. Hetty had agreed with that, but had said there was simply no reason why he couldn't, or wouldn't. When did *I* find it difficult to swallow? A sore throat: well, if he had, water would have gone down. Ulcers? I tried to look in his mouth again, but it caused so much distress I gave up. The dentist! I hated the dentist for one reason only, when I was a kid. Whereas now they have a sort of mini vacuum spatula to dredge up the saliva, time was when all the gear wedged about my jaws would stop me swallowing and I had to have a great hook hung over the edge. Something inside the mouth . . . something Hetty might have missed when she looked at his teeth and pronounced them healthy.

I found a torch and wedged it close. Then I said, "I'm sorry Smudgie-love. I have to do this. It may be uncomfortable but it won't take a moment," just like Mr Molar in Happy Families.

Smudge put up little resistance. He was too weak. I pushed a finger inside and found his tongue low in the mouth. Hating every move, I felt gingerly behind the teeth close to the jaw and he winced. My finger touched something soft, long – wool! A long piece of wool! I traced it back and back up the row of teeth to the end of the jaw – and there was what I was looking for . . .

No explorer sighting land on the horizon was ever more moved by emotion. My fingers worked away, my hand shaking only slightly with excitement. The operation was delicate in the extreme. One false move and anything could happen. I was on a borderline between life and death. And then it was over. I withdrew from the mouth a short darning-needle and length of brown wool. We were both trembling.

First I hugged the patient while tears flooded his woolly head. Then I sat back and watched, as he tried swallowing, very slowly, as if for the first time. The tail moved, weakly, joyfully. I lifted him into his basket and he licked my hand. Life was coming back to the brown eyes: sheer relief from despair was doing more than medical treatment could ever have achieved.

The tongue would be sore a while, scratched and torn and painful, but it would heal. I rushed down and fetched a bowl of water, the minced meat, and some chicken from a tin saved for a special occasion. Occasions came no more special than this.

He ate, a little at a time, very slowly, but the plate was cleared and the egg and milk that followed was easier. I washed his whiskers, bathed his eyes, gently brushed the shaggy coat and ears. I felt like Christiaan Barnard on his first transplant. Now for Hetty. This was the supreme moment, the proof that would stand me an inch higher than she was. At last.

I prayed she would be in, but her assistant answered the phone. Hetty was on an emergency call.

I said casually, "Ask her to give me a ring later, when she's free, will you?"

"Is it Smudge?"

"Yes, that's right. I'd like her to come and see him tomorrow."

"You're giving up, too?"

"It's not necessary."

"You mean he's *dead*?"

I exulted, all bubbly inside. Outwardly calm, I said "No. Cured . . ."

"You – what? He's *what*?" It wasn't Hetty but it was balm and high scoring just the same.

"He's eaten his supper – minced tongue." Oh, dear! how terribly tactless! "And chicken and some egg and milk. I'm going slowly on quantity because he must be a bit diddy on the digestion by now."

"He's *eating*?"

I grew impatient. "That's what I said! No profiteroles and cream, of course, but maybe a liqueur with the coffee."

"You don't mean it?"

"Not the liqueur, no. I don't approve of alcohol for four-year-olds, but I do think . . ."

"*How*, though? I mean – well, how? Just a minute. I think this is her now . . ."

There was a door banging and some excited exchange before Hetty came to the phone and said, "I told you, didn't I?" She was very calm. "I just thought it might take a little longer, that's all." She didn't even ask what I found wrong.

I went to bed at midnight. Nothing was so relaxing as to sit there and watch Smudgie getting better by the minute: sleeping contentedly, enjoying a drink, taking a short, bold, if somewhat unsteady, totter round the terrace outside. And all the time smiling at me, telling me with his eyes and tail how grateful he was. Nothing is as sad as a sick animal. Even a child can indicate pain, express discomfort and ease it with noisy protest. A dog suffers in silence, a silence much more devastating to watch than the pressures of pain. More and more I could understand Hetty's change in training from human to veterinary work.

She came over at teatime the following day. I'd waited with a wild impatience and half an eye on the drive all the time, causing Ben to suggest I took a stool and sat by the roadside, telling fortunes to while away the hours. And when Hetty did arrive, she spent the first five minutes asking Ben about Eric who was now beginning to emerge in short forays into the larder.

Eventually she asked about Smudge. I brought him in, with triumph. "A darning needle," I said, shrugging. "A bloody great darning needle. God knows how anybody missed it! Between two teeth with a length of brown wool. You imagine trying to swallow with that stuck in your wisdoms! Every move of the tongue would scratch, and if you swallow the needle would go down, too. A smart cookie like our Smudge wasn't going to risk that. He relied on another smart cookie to get it out. Me, for instance?"

Hetty would have had every right to resent such arrogance, but instead she was utterly delighted. She gave us both a kiss and said, "You know what, don't you? You're bloody marvellous!" I preened a little.

"It's not what you might call psychiatric work, though," I said, the Nobel Prize out of reach again. "Not the stuff to get the Golden Shrink Couch Of The Year Award, exactly."

"I don't know," said Hetty, slowly. "It wasn't, I agree, Smudge's psychiatric problem so much as your perception and logical reasoning. I'd say that qualified on a point of deviation." We giggled.

"Now I'll ring his people," said Hetty practically, "and give 'em the good news."

"You didn't do that last night?" I said, amazed and rather annoyed.

"Certainly not. I had to actually see him and be sure, didn't I? Not that I doubted your word, of course, but I'm directly responsible, and anyway, I thought they might decide it had all been a bit too easy!"

"Well, maybe he ought to stay another night. Get him back to normal."

"Earn you another fiver or two . . ."

I said, sharply, "No, not that. It's that he shouldn't go till he's good and ready." But the cash, as they say, sounded real pretty just the same.

"Look, you'll learn something doing this," Hetty said. "And it's something psychological about people. They only truly value what costs big money. Your name and reputation, their status among friends, it's all going to level up with the size of the bills." She watched my expression. "They can afford it, and more. You need it. Add your time, expertise, knowledge, experience, suffering, fondness, everything you're offering, plus their relief and gratitude. Why, you're doing them a favour in easing their conscience!"

I stopped being a noble hypocrite. Wasn't I the greatest, anyway?

"Your next Case," said Hetty, gathering up her things, "is ready. I said you were tied up for a day or two with an urgent assignment. They're waiting by the phone to hear something. I'll get in touch tomorrow. Notify you." With a curt nod she was gone. I never did know when Hetty was kidding.

Only this time she wasn't. She rang the following day, just as I was cleaning out the parakeet cage and the cockatoo perch. Clancy, the cockatoo, was staying a month. Luckily he was pretty good-natured though his beak was quite scary at first sight. The parakeets were housed in what amounted to a miniature aviary: there were four of them, and one seemed to be so unpopular with the rest that I took it out and put it in a spare cage I had. I couldn't bear the way they all shouted at it when it sulked in a corner nor the way they flew at it, pecking. In the first few days, it lost a lot of feathers and I was so afraid they might draw blood I had to do something. Now it sat in the cage by itself and moped in a corner, while the other three shouted at it from the aviary. I wondered what was wrong with it: I should have been able to analyse the problem, under my new hat as Animal Psychiatrist, but so far experience fought shy of including parakeets.

Ben was quite fond of Clancy. They indulged in a bit of backchat from time to time, but he was busy at that moment with his Top of the Pops Dog List. This was drawn up every week and pinned to the cupboard door. Rover was usually No 1 – our oldest inhabitant and unable to lose marks by chasing the hens or barking at Baby. Awards won were counted in chocolate drops.

Midsummer was way behind. Michaelmas Day well ahead, but the weather seemed to have settled for eternal summer. Holidays were slowing down and if less pets arrived, at least cheques came in for a greater number that left. In the field with Bubbles, we had a donkey who was liable to be a permanent resident. I had only refused two applicants – a monkey and a snake. Intuition told me both spelt trouble. I didn't regret revenue lost through self-preservation.

Marsha was in Morocco with a "sweet feller in fancy footwear" she told me. I said he sounded as if he might toe the line, ho-ho, and she said rather crossly that he manufactured shoes, if I had to be obtuse. He'd taken her shopping first and she was loaded with Pucci and Gucci and some Fiorucci . . . We had both laughed, but I detected a hint of regret. She said abruptly she would much rather be coming to help me. "Nothing's much fun," she said wistfully, "and the footsie feller looks like being a nothing bore."

I didn't point out she didn't have to go. Marsha did have to go. Her life was on those tramlines, mine was on these. That's the way the trolly goes.

Again I told her about my success with Smudge, but it was small fry to someone successful with fellers in fancy footwear, trombonists and group guys, as she called them. It's Tough at the Top, of course. Just trying to keep above the rest. When I said, somewhat patronisingly, to Hetty, "The trouble with vets is they don't hear the bark for the rustle of the leaves," (meaning textbooks, of course) which I thought terribly smart she gave me a long appraising look, raised elegant eyebrows and muttered, "Or the trunk for the limbs, perhaps?" and it took me ages to realise it wasn't even smarter.

Rajah was the fattest spaniel outside the *Guinness Book of Records*. Hetty led him slowly up the garden path, undercarriage low on the ground.

"Result of Breed Prejudice," she said indignantly. "Came with an ingrowing claw. Just as well, or no one would have stopped him eating and sleeping his way into that great dog basket in the sky."

"Why the breed prejudice?" I wanted to know. I bent to stroke him. He puffed like a chimney. His eyes were bleary, his coat dull.

"They always had greyhounds – actually raced them, years ago.

Someone gave their small daughter the spaniel puppy and they just can't be bothered with it. In some perverse way they seem to enjoy overfeeding and then recalling the slim elegance of their favourite breed. Like a lot of owners, they aren't so much cruel as uncaring. Except the little girl: she adores Rajah. He's all she's got because they're out a lot, both working. She's got a withered leg, too. Can only get about slowly. That's a disappointment to them, so they resent her feeling for the dog. I don't know, it just seems a domestic problem, emotional. You might be able to understand. He needs to lose a lot of weight and sleep less . . . sounds easy, but it has to be gradual, of course, and he won't like it."

She looked at me. Hetty knew my feelings about depriving dogs of tit-bits "for their own good". Hard enough when you can explain to an understanding human, but an emotional crisis for a loved pet who sees food as much an extension of your affection as the pat on the head and the kind word.

"He spends all his time with the little girl: she won't walk, so he doesn't. She's spoilt on sweets and cakes: so he is. The parents grow more critical of his sluggishness, unspeakable halitosis and contrast with their beloved greyhounds, but Emily, the daughter, adores him – fat, smelly and dull as he is. When he had to come to me for his claw, they asked me to do something about his general condition, and after a few questions I suggested you. Emily could never have been persuaded. She's only eight. She has lessons at home. A very lonely child."

"It's going to take time," I said. Like wittling away Mount Everest.

"They're going on holiday. I suggest lean meat, no extras but dog meal, and not much of that. One small dinner a day. You only have to get his weight down."

"Rubbish!" I said heatedly. "I have to help him lose weight, which is fairly easy, but I have to maintain his morale as well, which isn't." Hetty shrugged. I added, "Personally, I'd rather be overweight and happy than Twiggish, a hundred and suicidal."

"But he's not all that happy." I had to agree. He was puffing like a kettle. His eyes were slimy and dull. They followed Rosie nosing under bushes, with envy. I poured some tea from the china coffeepot. It poured with the idle grace of an Indian on a plantation, so I had stopped looking for the teapot.

Ben was making Cowboy Stew with plenty of baked beans and black treacle. I watched Rajah's nose twitch. I wished we were having salad which smells like cold water.

In the next few days, Fatty snuffled and panted and huffed and puffed and flopped and Ben got it down on tape and I cosseted Rajah on cuddles (reluctantly, his coat emanated bad health) and hand-outs of meal or lean beef in tiny pieces. He looked at me appealingly from time to time and I yearned to fill him up with something harmless, but there was nothing in which some calorie or carbohydrate didn't lurk. I gave all the dogs a covering of bran on their food, and doubled it for Rajah. I knew from my own bitter experience in the past that there is no way to lose weight other than to cut down on eating.

It was Ben who suggested carrot. If he's really starving hungry, he argued, anyone would eat carrot or celery or lettuce, even Rajah. Most dogs like *some* veg. I sliced up a carrot and tried it. Rajah wolfed it happily. Now his main meal was larger, with grated carrot and celery, and between times he could have a slice from the salad to show we loved him.

He looked longingly at the chocolate drops when the jar came out. I tried to do it out of sight, but his nose twitched when the lid came off, wherever it was. Ben, again, came to the rescue. "It's the smell that's so appetising. Like roast joints and stews to us." Then he said he had an idea and could he have the kitchen to himself (and a handful of dogs, including the inevitable Rover) for a while?

He came up with "Mock Doggy-chox – for Fido's Finer Figure." We never realised, that first day, what a valuable sideline we had in front of us.

I believe he boiled up carrots with bran, put the result through the blender, rolled it into little balls and then, when cool, sprinkled them very very lightly with cocoa. They certainly smelled faintly of chocolate but, to me, of carrot and bran as well. However the dogs didn't care. They loved them.

After the first trial run, I suggested Ben should keep me supplied. It saved a fortune on the real thing and did the dogs a great deal more good, if they were even the slightest overweight. We agreed I should supply ingredients, he would do the manufacturing, I would pay a small sum per hundred, but what I didn't foresee was his export trade. When he went down for tea with his aunts on Sunday, he talked them into ordering for resale in the shop, even begging suitable containers. He then designed his own label – a Yorkshire terrier rampant upon a pedigree, holding a Mock-Choc in his mouth, called "BEN'S MOCK DOG-CHOX. THE SWEET TREAT THAT LACKS FATS". They sold so quickly and easily that we had to agree to split profits and Ben was too busy to cook for us any more. This was, in its way, also a good thing, because it meant we were back on salads or poached eggs and I could join Rajah in slipping off a few urgent pounds myself.

The Colonel had rung with further apologies about Rover. His wife, he said, was still too ill to be left, but as the doctors assured him she was on the mend, he hoped to be home in just a week or two. He would then collect Rover and after a rest both of them would go back to be with her. I whispered it all to Rover who seemed by now resigned to anything. I had stopped worrying every time he was still, knowing it to be the serenity of advanced age.

Three or four times a day I took Rajah for short walks, using Toffee, a long, treacly dachshund with a buoyancy and charm which appealed to everyone, as front man. He would bowl along on his ridiculous little legs, urging Rajah, who admired him for his Giacometti lines, to join him.

Humphrey said there was a distinct improvement. He was always full of advice. His wife, Ireen, was a herbalist and I now had a shelf full of such things as Dill Water (for Fido's flatulence?), Rue (to cure poultry of moult) and Feverfew (to be on the safe side, he said, hinting at raging lurgies). But Ben swore her Dandelion Lotion had cured his acne, and her Rosemary Rinse was making hay of his dandruff. He was negotiating a deal for marketing, with personal recommendations.

The news from the West was slight and irregular. He said he was Fine. I said I was Fine, too. He said the weather was on the change: I didn't say I was too. I said it would soon be winter, hinting at "what then?" But the calls were short and unproductive, cool and disinterested. It was always "someone else's phone" and they appeared to be always hovering in earshot. I suggested a call box and he did try that, but it was worse, with pips every time I tried to make any real contact.

Since Toby had left, Lady had taken over. She obviously considered it her duty to look after me. The torch had been handed on. I had become very very fond of Lady. Not just because she was such an agreeable dog, but because she made me laugh. She was a great bundle of a dog. A mass of woolly curls. A grown-up puppy. She leapt alert at the sound of the phone, and glanced at me anxiously, longing to protect me from its threatening sneers. Sometimes in the evening she would jump to her feet, shoot out of the back door, hurtle round a rose-bed a few times and then come in to flop down and sleep soundly the rest of the night. Vague but happy memories floated from her subconscious, and recognising times past for that one instant helped her adjust to times present. Dogs have a lot to teach those clinging to What Has Been.

As soon as I reported Rajah's new routine and the loss of the first pound, Hetty came along with another Case. Rajah, she argued, was merely a matter of regulating food intake. Nelson was more in my current line of specialised work as a psychiatric vet.

Nelson was one of the world's soap-boxers. The Hilda Ogden of the Dog World. He had something to say on every occasion, and it was usually aggressive. He was a Yorkshire Terrier – small, whiskery, cuddly and adorable. That is, until he began barking. One woof and he was away, like an eight-day clock he didn't run down until he couldn't keep it up any longer. The other dogs barked a greeting, a warning, or for attention. They could be silenced at a word, but nothing – *nothing* – stopped Nelson.

His owner lived in a block of flats and was in trouble with neighbours. She brought him to me herself on Hetty's advice. "He gets hysterical," said the girl, huge dark eyes as blue as the Oxford Crew after losing a Boat Race. "Once he starts, which is usually when he wakes up and isn't eating, he never stops."

He had been a wedding present from her husband, an officer in the Merchant Navy. He was to keep her company when he was away. She was so in love with him (the dog – she didn't mention the husband) she took him with them on their honeymoon. They had rented a small cottage and he had to be shut in the bathroom.

"He wanted to get in bed between us," she explained, "and even when we gave up and let him, he still went on barking. I think he wanted my husband to get out and sleep in the basket. In the end we put his bed in the bathroom and he just stood inside by the door and barked non-stop all night. We had no proper honeymoon at all. He ruined it. We quarrelled all the time about what we should do. My husband's proposals were unspeakable!" The husband was due back from the sea soon. It would become a choice between the two of them and I had a fair idea, from the way she kissed Nelson, who was going to win.

He was so gorgeous I wanted to hug him all the time. He hated that. He wasn't satisfied with protesting verbally, he ran at ankles. It's all part of a mild hysteria which starts from too little control as a puppy and once it takes hold, they've become too confused and overwrought to change.

The girl assured me she had tried all the usual things. Banishment on first bark: a smack: a noisy newspaper. Her brother, staying with her, had been less gentle but with even the wildest wallop Nelson never stopped barking. Hysteria is a difficult problem and I consulted Humphrey. There might, of course, be a herb for it.

He sat at the table spilling his tea because, he said, the wind of the sea always affected his palsy. "You could try sage. Rosemary or lavender might 'elp, too." The smoke from his cigarette curled into his plastic eye. Nelson barked on and on.

I shouted "*Anything*, Humphrey," and meant it. "A drug, say, like opium. Would Californian poppies do?" They ran wild in the kitchen garden, along with everything else. Nelson stopped for a moment and, in the brief pause, bit Humphrey's ankle.

Humphrey landed a firm kick which hardly affected Nelson at all. "Ireen would say hop, but I'm not sure." It sounded too energetic for me. "Rue, now, or Caraway Tea, four times a day like. An' if that don't do nothing, go for Gentian."

But he wasn't really confident and neither was I. It sounded too chancy and took too long. It had to be something immediate, like cyanide.

"They do say round here as 'a dog in the wind don't bark'," he offered helpfully. "When he opens 'is mouth the wind takes 'is breath away, see?" I suppose there was a more subtle interpretation, too, but I failed to see what it was. And you couldn't guarantee a steady nor'easter in a honeymoon cottage twenty-four hours a day.

I thanked him, and watched as he weaved his way down the drive, one-eyed, and with one idea in his head – to reach the next address before their coffee grew cold. Humphrey operated on continual refills of hot liquid, much as the combustion engine runs on refills of petrol. He left behind the germ of an idea with me, too . . .

I blew. Dogs hate being blown at. It's partly because it takes them by surprise; partly because it's too nebulous an attack for counter measures. You can't snap at a puff of air. After two days I was breathless, but Nelson had the message. Before he began to open his mouth to bark he would glance at me: I would take a long breath and he would stop, turn round and walk away in silence. I kept him with me a week and by the end of it he was only after ankles. I tried blowing for that, too, but it took the double joints of a contortionist, and I decided to merely pass on the tip to his owner. After all, I'd been asked to cope with the Bark not the Bite, and that was what I'd done.

The gorgeous girl with the sea-blue eyes arrived to collect him, bringing an equally gorgeous man I took to be Rupert, her husband. They had a suitcase in the car and said they were off for the weekend. I suggested Nelson should sleep on his own, just to be on the safe side. They exchanged amused glances. I could see my advice was totally unnecessary. A second, more successful honeymoon, I thought. "Such a unique present for you to give the bride," I said as we reached the car. The young man turned, surprised. "*I* gave her a hostess trolley," he said, and I realised he wasn't 'old Roo' after all, but the Best Man. In point of fact, I'm sure he wasn't – who would choose a hostess trolley in preference to a Yorkshire terrier, even a non-stop barking one? I rather hoped Nelson would have a go at his pyjama trousers.

Ruthless, the alsatian afraid of cats, went the following morning. Several other boarders left. The house began to develop a hollow ring. I got to bed by ten. I could lie in till eight. I felt superfluous. Not needed on Voyage, like a lawn-mower at Christmas.

Christmas! Without a word from the West Country, too proud to prod, deserted like the last rat on a buoyant boat, Christmas was going to be something I would have to face alone, unless, perhaps, I suggested Angharad Rees of the tender touch and winning ways should join us. Huh! I thought, I bet she'd never think of blowing at barkers! We all have our talents, after all.

Ben was inventing what he proposed to call a Fido-Tidy – a plastic version of the hospital bottle to be held in place by a dainty harness. It was for "The Lazy Leg-Lifter" and would save, he reckoned, innumerable homes from ruined carpets and relationships both before and after training. Ben had turned out to be a boy of imagination, enterprise and quite amazing innovation, most of it brought out by enforced incarceration in a challenging environment.

Just the same it was hard to get away from a sense of impending doom and gloom. Doom, with its hint of sinister undercurrents, would be preferable. Gloom only spells boredom, lack of purpose, a nothingness.

However chaotic and exhausting the past few months might have been, it was still better than looking to a future as bland as bread pudding. I watched the Motorway taunting me with beckoning lights until it was hard to resist following them.

I had to put myself to bed with some of Ireen's recommended Sticky Willy Mixture.

18

The redecorating was far from easy. Wet paint attracted flies, gnats, dogs and Ben's elbows. I kept feeling my temper slipping and that shocked me. Usually everybody's Pollyanna, with a smile and a song, guaranteeing all the horrors of early morning cheer and a jolly joke when the roof falls in, I was my own sunny comforter if nobody else's. Now, suddenly, I was quite normally unspeakable from time to time, sulking when the baker left brown wholemeal – which is so blameless I hate it – instead of my nice gooey sliced white. I grumbled at Frilly when she put a paw in the pancake batter, and I shouted at Pathos when he brought in a dead frog and placed it lovingly on Ben's boots.

Humphrey's friend, Oliver, was to come in and do the ceilings for me. "A real little Mickey Angel on ceilings," Humphrey promised. That sounded good enough to someone who not only worked in the occasional dead fly and festooned cobweb with the brush, but also any unwary spider unable to run quick enough to escape. The frog would have gone the same way had Pathos put it in my unwavering path.

Between us all I felt we could complete the house before winter set in. Perhaps even before Ben went back to school, a fate neither of us cared to mention. The Misses Priddle were soon selling up and moving to Newhaven: life was in the process of lurching off course for a time. I didn't like it at all. But when I woke next morning the sun was streaming through the windows for what might be the final fling of summer. I lay awake and alone, except for the current relay of home-comforted dogs, and saw nothing but ruin around me. Once Ben had gone, the boarders had gone, the summer had gone, what would be left to take their place? The occasional psychiatric patient? I was rapidly becoming one myself . . . but at the bitching hour of seven, even for me dread springs eternal sometimes. I needed a lie-in or a day out, I decided. Something to get me away from the goats to be milked, hens to be fed, Baby honking for love, but weren't we all doing just that? I got up and dressed, yawning.

Despair turned to decision over hot rolls and farm butter. I remembered a coach left the village at eleven o'clock for the nearest stretch of coastline. I suddenly made up my mind, grabbed a bikini, purse, towel and Ben's bike, propped a note on the kitchen table to warn Ben – and ran away.

The sense of sudden freedom went to my head. I whizzed down

the slope to the village at the speed of sound, putting out of my head all the possible risks and horrors of home. "A lovely day," I said fondly to the conductor, a man with alternate sides to his face as unlike as two love affairs. "Return ticket please. What time can I get a bus back? About one, say?" That would give me nearly an hour and a half to swim, sample the local cuisine, find myself a bronzed lifeguard and make a fool of myself.

"Free," he said, using the side of his mouth that drooped into an unshaved chin.

"At last!" I agreed, wondering how he knew about my smart move away from captivity. "Would there be a bus around lunch-time?" But he turned a deaf, outsize ear, and went down the bus to a lady knitting a Fair Isle carpet. On the way back he said, ". . . 'ave to be free. Nuffin' before," and the other side of his profile smirked in triumph. The elation died. Suppose Ben didn't wake up till midday? And suppose the lurcher got at the rabbits? Baby might snout defenceless Rajah? Somebody might even open Joanna Southcott's Box and all those awful things they predict – like death, famine and untold distress – would be upon us! Rover might actually die at last! I was in a state bordering on panic when the sea finally appeared, shimmering and careless and offering an easy way out. . . . I leapt off at the first Stop on the Promenade.

I rushed about in search of a phone. I could, at least, try to wake Ben. I could warn him, beg him, bribe him, even perhaps ring for some taxi to get me back. Every phone box was out of order, like a row of red-faced Victorian ladies ravished and deserted. On the end one, someone had daubed, "Joe is a Slob" which I ticked with my lipstick before running on to find some more.

Every corner had a selection of lavatories, but never another phone box. I decided to see Mr Posford. Mr Posford managed one of the hotels who recommended me to their dog-parking clients. He always sounded very nice on the phone. His letters assured me of his co-operation at all times. Now was his big chance.

The strap on my sandal gave way just before I reached the Grand Miramar. I hobbled in and found him talking to the receptionist. They looked a little surprised, especially when I introduced myself, but he recovered quickly enough to offer me a drink. I was hoping for lunch, but the drink was at least an opening gambit. It was just that anxiety, hobbling and making love all leave me terribly hungry. I had the experience of two of these and the third might be on the cards if only Mr Posford had looked more like Ross Washington. As he wasn't, food seemed a promising alternative.

I decided it was hardly worth phoning home now. I might just catch Ben at the parakeet cage and he'd leave the door ajar as he answered the phone and the birds would escape to be eaten by Frilly who would go mad with a quill stuck in her throat and attack Rover. Or something.

Mr Posford ordered me a Martini and then excused himself. He was, he said, very busy. I hid my disappointment about the lunch, ate up all the peanuts on the bar and finished my drink. Then I went to the beach. I would, at least, get some sunshine and sea air, even if I didn't get a lifeguard.

The beach was only just keeping its level under a howling Force 9 gale. Hats, towels and windbreaks rose and fell and sailed away and were retrieved. I clung to my own possessions and tried to shelter behind a breakwater, shivering and with sand flung into my mouth every time someone boldly leapt over me. The lower I got, the safer I seemed. I must have been out of sight when I heard voices suggesting settlement on the other side. I recognised the woman's right away. She was less than six foot from my ear.

"Frankly, I don't know how Winnie could. Darling, do cover it up. It's going to be no use to me covered in sand. But Winnie is always so trusting." The woman's name was Willis. She had come with her sister to leave two canaries and then argued about the fee when they came back, weeks later. Her reason was the fact that they ate so little it could hardly have cost me a thing. Somehow she overlooked the responsibility, daily cleaning, health checks and the continual trilling I had to endure.

"To leave them with a woman like *that*!" she went on. "And she had the nerve to charge over and above any seed she might have had to buy, yet what work is there with Sweetie-pie and Snozzleguts . . ." I remembered thinking that with names like that, even canaries had to be bad news.

The woman went on: "She told Louise that George could sleep with her if he liked! I wouldn't have George anywhere near *my* bed, smelly beast! And when Lou asked her to make sure and check on his, er, well, his 'paperwork' (you know what I mean!) she simply laughed!" I remembered the euphemism: the woman had actually winced when I asked if she really meant bowel movements. George, a happy sweet-natured spaniel was a lot nicer than any of them. He wouldn't have gone within a mile of Louise's friend.

The man said, after a short pause, "I'll put it away. You're not really interested in it at all, are you?" He sounded rather hurt.

I waited agog for the answer. She said loftily, "I just think it's rather silly. Specially on a beach. You can play with it by yourself, later."

The wind tossed a paper bag over the breakwater. For an instant, a hand appeared to retrieve it, followed by a face and our eyes met. We stared at one another, only inches apart, then her startled expression vanished and the whispering showed I was recognised.

There was going to be nothing else to hear now, and as the gale was trying to tear the bikini from me, as well as my hair by the roots, I got up to go and allowed myself a quick look at the couple, now silent, beyond. Plump and well-covered, she clung grimly to a low canvas chair, hidden under sunglasses and thick coat. Beside her lay a skinny man in shorts and goose pimples, with a metal detector half-covered by his jacket.

I rang Ben from the bus station. I was cold, hungry and tired. There was music in the background and I could hear an occasional bark. More than anything in the world I wanted to be there. Ben said, "Hullo. Having fun?" His mouth was full of baked beans.

"No. I bet you are though!" I wailed.

"Of course. How's the sea? Bringing back a lifeguard, are we?"

I said bitterly, "The sea is lethal, as my right foot, now frost-bitten and wearing a broken sandal, can prove. All lifeguards have wisely gone with the wind. I'm hungry!"

Ben said soothingly, "Come home, all is forgiven. We've had a few phone calls – nothing too hairy. I took a prickle out of Smokey's paw. Done everything you didn't. Frilly's up the lilac tree after a squirrel. I dropped the lid of the brown casserole."

I didn't ask if it was broken. It was broken. "Business as usual, in fact," I said, strangely comforted. No good fussing over Frilly, she could get down from anywhere after playing hard to get and watching me do my nut. "Bus goes in a minute."

On the way home, Miss Bloomer, housekeeper at the Vicarage, sat next to me. She leant over and murmured discreetly, "And how's the little venture?"

"Fantastic," I claimed, embarrassed. "Absolutely fantastic!" I don't know why I exaggerated like that. Low voices make me uneasy. "How many do you have now?" she queried. Her breath smelled of hot felt hats and her jumper of dead violets.

"Oh, goodness, about a dozen I think," I said airily as if only my Head Kennelman could be expected to know.

"Such a job to feed, I expect?" I shook my head. Villagers have an antique right to be nosy. Or think they have.

"No, no," I said. "They're not fussy once they see food up for grabs, though newcomers and the very slow get theirs apart, of course. And I get stale bread from the baker which helps a lot;

usually brown and baked in the oven, it's better than biscuits really."

She raised her eyebrows. "Yes, yes, of course. Do you take them out at all?"

I felt quite shocked. What *did* she expect? "I make sure they go in the Exercise Yard for an hour every day," I said firmly, "and of course we have at least one walk however bad the weather, even if it has to be in relays. They sometimes run loose. We're well walled-in, you know. It's almost impossible to escape."

A short silence fell. Then she said, "A lot of washing to do, though?"

Patiently I replied, "Not a lot. They don't often need a bath while they're with me and they bring their own blankets. I give them a good shake every day, of course. They prefer them a bit smelly I think."

There was a long pause. "And how's dear Benny?" she asked anxiously.

"An enormous help," I said enthusiastically. "Very fond of them all, too. Shares his bed with three of them at the moment. Prue, she's a little Tibetan, used to snuggle right down under the blankets with him and he loved it! Miss Pringle laughed about that when we told her!"

I could see at once she didn't approve of dogs on beds. Her face was pale and her expression wooden to say the least, making her sharp nose like a garden hoe about to rake me over. I went on in self-defence, "They absolutely love him, and he doesn't seem to miss the company of other boys at all."

"But don't you board both sexes?" she asked, more icily than ever.

"Dogs and bitches, of course," I said puzzled.

There was a much longer silence between us. Then she said, "The vicar and I thought you took in children on adventure holidays, a sort of camp, perhaps . . ."

I cycled home like a jet off the runway. I wished I had a stick of rock for Ben, or a tan, or even a menu. Something to prove everybody else was right and I certainly had needed a day off. As things were, I felt I never wanted another as long as I lived. It had done wonders to prove the superiority of routine.

19

When I got back, a child was sitting on the garden seat. A little girl in a long, frilled skirt, round glasses, and a pigtail. Rajah sat, looking up at her adoringly.

I said "Hullo. You're Emily." Why wasn't she on holiday? I sat next to her. She was very pale, thin, serious.

"Mummy and Daddy dropped me here. They went on to see Auntie Joyce. They said they'll pick me up on the way back." She looked at me apologetically. "I was sad without Rajah."

"He missed you too," I said. "I thought you were going away?"

"No. I don't want to go. I want to take Rajah home with me and be there. I hate hotels."

I said with every sympathy, "So do I!" then, "I'll get us some tea."

Ben was at the back door. "Hetty just rang up" he said. "The Colonel died this morning."

"His wife," I corrected, hurrying past.

Ben said sadly, "No, the Colonel. From a heart attack."

I stared at him, stopping at the sink, kettle outstretched, everything frozen in a sudden Ice Age of shock. The Colonel's wife was expected to die; Rover was always on the brink of dying. But that brisk, upright support for them both . . . I stayed rock still. There were worse things than a day at the seaside. I went, at last, to kneel by Rover's box. His eyes were closed and his breathing was shallow. This time, I thought, he probably means it. I stroked his head and cried a little. Rover was just waiting now. He would put up no further fight. He was released from a long vigil.

Ben led me back into the garden. "I'll get the tea," he said. "By the way, a man called Pendle wants to leave a tame fox and a small turtle for a few days. He's from Mrs Sissingtons. The Willoughbys are coming for Bobby about eight and will you ring your husband after six." Oh, my God! I thought, I bet he's coming home. He'll find his house full of paint pots, his bed full of dogs and his bath full of turtles. There was only the loo left for the fox.

"Two ducks seem to be missing," continued Ben, "and Humphrey called with some of Ireen's Agrimony Tisane. She thought you might be in need of a tonic." So she was psychic as well as a herbalist! I was urgently in need of something. ". . . and he said 'Badgers'!"

"And badgers to him, too," I said wearily. "We don't have any."

"We do, in holes under trees, laying in winter supplies. Like duck with pondwater sauce!" I didn't even shudder. The ducks, a further gift via Hetty, were inclined to wander. They usually came back at bedtime unless it rained very hard when they had to be found or they just sheltered under a hedge. Ducks may use the highway by law, but not hens, and I'm sure they know this. Ducks, you see, were always driven to market on their own flat feet. Hens were carried.

"And Emily?"

"She's OK. She's really quite OK." He sounded surprised. I said "I'd better ring my husband." If there was something I ought to know I could lump it in with the rest. For once he answered the phone.

"You rang." I said, after the I'm fine too, routine.

"Yes," he said. Then, suspiciously, "You were out!"

It was an accusation. I ignored it. He, himself, was hardly ever in.

"Yes," I said. "What's up?"

"My leg." His tone changed to one of suffering humanity. "Up on a stool. I told you about my bad fall." He had told me nothing at all except he was fine. "Over the stick I was using because my ankle went lame after I tripped while cutting my toenails? Well, I'm suspected of a small fracture and I go for an X-ray tomorrow." So it sounded genuine. The sort of thing he alone could do. One of his honest dodges to get out of hard work this end. Maybe he was accident-prone from being subconsciously psychosomatic. I was wearing my psychiatrist's hat again. All these delays in facing a debate, even, on the remote possibility of coming home, were unavoidable for him. At least I'd have time to get the turtle out of the towels. Perhaps even the turkey out of the oven, before he made it.

We all had tea together. I tried to explain to Emily just why Rajah had to stop being fed sweets and sticky buns. I was rather brutal but kids understand black and white, so I said, "If he goes on eating too much, he will be so ill he might die." I showed her Ben's Mock-Chox and she ate two or three. I wondered if she might fancy a trotter later on. Her mind seemed miles away and though she listened, I doubt whether she took in a thing.

When her parents arrived, she was far less relaxed. She said clearly and quite simply that she wouldn't go home. No, she announced with the firm conviction of a mature child of nine, often indulged, she wanted to stay here. She hated hotels. She hated Dubrovnik. She hated beaches. She had walked to the pond with Ben, helped find the two missing ducks (beak-under-wing in long grass, a prey for anything, like teenagers from Tyneside trusting to luck in the Big City) and she had washed-up. She might have been recounting her adventures in Disneyland. She had helped feed the dogs, carried a bucket to Baby, mucked in and loved it.

We tried every possible persuasion to get her to go but in the end I said, "Right, let her stay. But she'll have to work jolly hard and we don't go overboard on luxury food. No sticky buns – it's beans on toast, eggs, Shreddies and sardines with a lot of salad from the garden and milk from the goats. What's more, you get it yourself during the day. You don't like hotels, Emily, well, I have news for you! This is anything but!" She was delighted.

Secretly I think her parents felt the same way. They insisted I accept hotel rates and now I was getting far too commercially minded to argue. I had long since realised that responsibility demands a high price. Emily moved into the small spare room with Rajah, and her luggage came next day. Miss Bloomer would never believe it about the dogs.

Just as Ben was looking for Mr Pendle's telephone number so I could talk my way out of the fox and turtle, he arrived with both. The fox was only a cub, and very, very sweet. The Willoughbys had taken Bobby and three more would leave during the week. I was beginning to dread the possibility of an empty house again.

Sidney, the unlikely name for anything so pretty, was welcomed. He was such a very jolly little fox. But he was terrified of the dogs. Maybe, before being orphaned, his mother had told him of the huntsman's horn, or deep inside dwelt the dread that all baby foxes are born with, besides their brush and whiskers. I had to carry him everywhere I went and the one time I put him down while I went to the loo, he let out such a heart-rending sound that even there I tucked him under my arm and promised never to let him go.

I had almost forgotten Lady *was* a boarder. She had been with us so long, fitted in so well. Her telephone reactions and occasional belt round a rosebush were so predictable. She had so many appealing ways: the roll-over on her back when one of us bent to tickle her; the way she liked to play hide and seek with Ben, who she recognised as an echo of her beloved Adam. I had sent photographs to him, staying the summer, much against his will, with his father in France, promising he could stay with us when he came back home for the final week of the holidays. I promised to speak to his mother about that. I felt sure she would agree. She seemed completely indifferent to the child. So when she rang me one morning, I was so surprised I could barely answer.

She had a low, cultured voice which rose abruptly to make a point, like a soprano being overtaken in a bus queue. She said she had only just heard I was keeping Adam's dog. She thought she should have been told. She was *most* surprised at this connivance between the boy and me. She would very much appreciate an explanation. Perhaps I would call round and see her.

I said perhaps she would call round and see me. I was a very busy lady and there was quite a lot to discuss.

She said, "And you don't think *I* am a busy lady, is that it?" as if being a busy lady was a term of virtue, like virginity.

I gave her the benefit of any minute doubt. "We're all extremely busy. I have tried so often to get you on the phone, I think you must be almost as busy as me!" (So busy, I didn't add, that you never noticed Lady was missing until now.)

"I have been in Italy. I am now going to New York. I have packing to do, undo and redo. I have to instruct my housekeeper about Adam's clothes for next term. I am very tired, and –" reading my thoughts with incredible accuracy – "so far as I am concerned, that dog was *always* missing." I recalled Adam saying he kept it out of sight for everybody's sake. As usual when thinking of Adam and Lady and their enforced separation, tears choked my larynx, and I said more gently, "So we're both busy. Do you run a car?" Competition was rife now, but I knew I held the winning hand.

She said, "Of course."

I said triumphantly, "I don't." Felix was still uninsured, untaxed and unhappily lurking in the small garage, so she said with a sigh, "Tomorrow at ten?" and I said I would look forward to it.

Emily's things arrived together with her doctor's phone number. Her case was packed with innumerable long skirts and a few pairs of jeans. "Skirts hide my leg," she said with a resignation I found very sad. And suddenly I knew why she hated hotels and holidays and being made to wear long skirts on a beach full of bikini-clad kids. I said I thought jeans would be best round the house and garden, doing the sort of work we did. So we folded the long ornate skirts and put them away for the duration. I planned to persuade her to turn up the legs of her jeans to the top of her wellies, and then later discard the wellies altogether and perhaps lift the legs of her trousers even higher until she was wearing shorts. Once she got some fresh air to the withered leg it might help it develop a bit as well as stop her from being so self-conscious about it. But we had plenty of time. We could let it happen gradually.

At ten to ten next morning, I tidied my hair, arranged a social smile (No. 2, I think. It was a long time since the list had been used) and sat in the loo reciting some pertinent lines from Blake's *Songs of Innocence*. Very calming. Very comforting. Such artificial aids should have been unnecessary with a summer of some success behind me, but the future threatened danger to any over-confidence. I didn't even change my bib-and-brace overalls.

Adam's mother was almost exactly as I pictured her, only younger. Tall, with dark rich hair and a very clear skin. Only her mouth gave her away as the self-centred lady she always proved herself. But then mouths give away everything. You can disguise eyes, fake shapes, conceal what's real – but a mouth defeats all craft and pretence and deceit.

She was tanned a sort of cinnamon warmth and her linen skirt was cut to flatter an already flattering figure. A silk shirt boasted the fact it was exclusive far more clearly than any inner label. She got out of a certain sort of car that usually has a certain sort of man to go with it. Both of them smooth, quiet, confident and well-tanked. Performance guaranteed.

"Hello," I said introducing myself and holding out a hand. Hers looked as if it never touched anything heavier than a drop of Patou's Joie. "Like some coffee? Fruit juice? Anything . . .?" I hoped she might opt for tap water. It's the one thing we have which can't be compared unfavourably with better brands.

"I'd love a cup of tea," she said. I was a bit thrown. I saw her as a Martini-with-a-Twist lady and we could only manage the twist. I called Emily and asked her to make us some tea and bring it to the garden. Already she was enjoying responsibility and if the limp tended to tip the tray a bit, we could always deposit any overflow in the pansy bed.

I asked about Adam. "He's fine," she said diffidently. "Sailing with his father at the moment, off Juan I think . . ."

"He's a smashing kid," I said enthusiastically. "We only met a few times but he writes such hilarious letters!"

She laughed ruefully. "Not to me, he doesn't. Only when prompted by his father to send a card."

"Well, they're for Lady really," I lied hastily. Lately Adam had poured out his heart to me about having to go to France, never being taken out on Open Days, missing his grandfather. "I did try to contact you by phone. I was uneasy about keeping Lady for Adam without your knowledge, but you were away and he was sure you would agree to what we thought best for her. Lady means such a lot to Adam."

"Well," she said with a sigh "thinking about it, of course, you did the right thing". She turned slightly and I caught her profile. It reminded me of a saluki called Pepper who came to us in a gem-studded collar and had never been given a bone.

"Then I'll go on keeping her here as long as you like," I said with relief. "We've grown very attached to her, all of us. She's a truly lovely character."

Lady came towards us, following Ben with the tea tray. He wore headphones and plimsolls. Emily limped alongside, carrying a plate of home-baked jumbles in imminent danger of decorating the aubrietia. There were formal introductions, then the two of them left, Emily breathing on her glasses and polishing them on the edge of her tee shirt.

I said uncomfortably, "Just staying here . . ."

"You take *children* as well?" You could see she thought I needed a straightjacket.

I said gloomily, "*and* turtles, small foxes, hens, ducks, goats . . ." I shrugged. "No snakes or monkeys though: I know my limitations."

There was a pause. Then she said sympathetically, "Oh, dear!" and I felt as if I'd been caught standing on my head rather well, but showing my knickers to do it.

She said, "Then perhaps you know what to do with a schoolboy at home? I mean, ought I to play cricket in the garden? Take him to skating rinks? Movies? I'm always at a loss when he's there." She sounded really anxious and I began to feel sorry for her – reluctantly, but with a glimmer of understanding.

"Most kids just want you to listen while they talk. Really listen, not just hear the babble. They like to share what you're doing, too. I don't think they want to go for formal outings or be played with. Maybe they could do with someone roughly their size and shape for that."

"So if Adam comes back home at all, and I'm away, could he come here?"

I stopped with my mouth open, checking immediate agreement. Dogs for a fortnight were one thing; little boys, however nice, for unspecified periods at regular intervals, another. Then I remembered it was Adam, and not just any nice little boy, and I said, "Of course! Any time at all, starting with the last week of the holidays, perhaps?"

She sighed and gave me her first really warm and genuine smile. "He had a nanny until he was eight. Since then it's been very difficult. I can't take him with me when I travel and housekeepers don't like children around. My father was very fond of him but when he died . . ." she shrugged, and I felt sorry for all of them. A father who had the boy because of 'legal rights'. A mother who found him an embarrassment, and a housekeeper who didn't like him at all. It was a good thing he had Lady. She must have read what I was thinking as I bent to fondle the dog's head. She was keeping a close watch on the guest and her ears were flat to show her uneasiness. I lifted and tickled them to show there was nothing to fear.

"You see?" she said. "Lady won't come to me . . ." Her voice was tinged with disappointment. "We hardly know one another. I do wish that I – but it's too late. Probably do more harm than good to make an effort I can't sustain. If only my mother had stayed on with us after the death of my father, or Adam's father had . . ." She paused, then appeared to put it all from her mind and gave me a warm smile. "The gardener gave Adam the dog when it was a puppy. I think he could see the boy was lonely. He said to Adam 'It's a lady Dog' and Adam called her Lady Dog from then on. He's always been such a funny little boy." She paused again. "But it's taken me such a long time to appreciate it."

We began to walk back to the car. I could almost like her now. It must have taken a lot to be so honest. "Don't worry," I said, "I'll see they're OK." Hetty would have said I was doing my God act as usual.

She held out a hand and we solemnly shook. It could have been the final frame from *Mrs Miniver Strikes Again*.

We waved goodbye without another word. Lady went mad with relief when we were alone again. Three times round the duckpond was nothing compared to this. I picked up the sinister skull of a mature pig which had been lying ostentatiously in front of us for most of the interview, and slung it over the hedge. It would doubtless come back in due course, delivered by some dutiful dog – my legendary Achilles heel or Gorgon's head.

In the post next morning was a cheque from Mrs Adair for £150. She hoped it would cover Lady's board throughout the summer and Adam's week or so with us at the end of his holiday. If Lady went on living with us in term time – and she hoped that would be possible – she proposed a similar amount would become payable at Christmas.

Was it conscience money? It was far, far too much. Ought I to send it back, or at least a part? A bit of my graffiti chalked near the window facing the Motorway read, "MONEY SHOULD CIRCULATE LIKE RAIN WATER". It wasn't one of Thornton Wilder's best quotes, but it kept my optimism rampant for that reckless future up the other end of the rainbow, and allowed me to order Kup cakes on Thursdays. I decided to pass on the cheque into Mr Wallaby's avaricious little hands and clear the final fog of my overdraft.

20

Rover died during the night. Something prompted me to go down when I woke suddenly in the early hours. The other dogs hardly stirred, which goes to show how very unnecessary deathbed gatherings can be. Animals accept death with as little fuss as they welcome birth.

I didn't want to disturb the others so I crept into the big old kitchen, with the ticking clock, occasionally creaking dog basket and long shadows falling between moonlight through the geraniums on the broad window-sill. I always went first to Rover when I came downstairs in the morning, half-dreading, half-expecting, wholly resigned. His breath was always shallow, his responses very slow. I knelt by the box now and ran my hand automatically round the inside to make sure that the old pillow, covered with his blanket, was adequate for the maximum comfort and was guarding his tired old body from the unrelenting but draught-proof sides. And as I did it, I knew he was dying. There was a flaccid feel about his skin, a strange unreality about the actual muscle structure, which pointed with unerring certainty to failure in a decreasing nervous system. Once, many years before, I had held my mother's hand and known, with a shock I never forgot, that her life was ending, even though until that minute I had merely thought of her as very ill.

Rover lay peacefully content to fade into the night. Tears ran down the side of my nose and dripped, like holy water as a benediction, on the thinning coat, the sad, sparse head and he stirred once, his eyes meeting mine and imploring me to understand he was on his way to find his old master again.

There was no point in ringing Hetty. Even if she could have done something to keep him alive a little longer, it was not what he would have wanted. For too long he'd been waiting for the reunion, too long he had stayed, watching the door, holding on until the Colonel walked back through it. Now he knew positions were reversed and somewhere, perhaps, the Colonel watched the golden gates for his old friend to come to him. Rover knew the Colonel was dead, of that I'm sure. He had been able to give up the vigil at last.

It was warm and quiet and I sat stroking gently for two hours, feeling the pulse flicker, flicker, like a fire in the grate as everyone leaves it for bed and sleep. And then it was no more. A little sigh and he was gone . . .

I drew a blanket over the box, but I stayed leaning against the warm Aga in a state of strange self-hypnosis, midway between reality and something beyond. The room was very still and only once, a little earlier, had there been any kind of movement. Just before Rover died, the back door had trembled as if from an early morning breeze – or as if someone had been there, about to enter.

And it was only later, when I forced myself to get up and stand, shivering a little in a thin dressing-gown, at the porch, seeing a mist rising with the first streaks of dawn over the sky, that I realised there was no wind, no breeze, no movement of air at all. And if there had been, the loose-fitting sash windows would have moved as well, and the trees outside, not just the back door, the focal point of the old dog's life for so long.

There was no point in going back to bed. I somehow hated to leave Rover, even though the real part of him had gone. The link between us had been so very strong. I felt a lot calmer than I had for some time, a lot less harrassed and fretful.

Hetty came and took him away before breakfast. I had given a lot of thought to burial, but it seemed somehow nothing more than a superfluous, even affected, gesture on my part. Hetty agreed. She said, "I've nothing against a small memorial, but frankly I think too much guff gets morbid. Plant something . . ." So I took a geranium from one of the pots which had stood on the sill near his box and I put it in the tub by the back door. I turfed out the dead bush, renewed the soil, put in the geranium, with nasturtiums for company. It was the wrong time of year to transfer them and I had no doubt they would be finished in a week or two, but oddly enough they lived on for longer than those in the bed they came from, seeded and reappeared the following year.

Four wire-haired terriers arrived as I was washing-up. "Sorry," the harrassed owner said, as one shot under her car, another towards the duckpond and two began a fight over the ball in their baggage. "Mr Grimble at Moth End was sure it would be all right. He said you take anything, any time at all."

She was going off to her sister who had fallen off a mountain. I think. Or was it the mountain that fell on her sister? I was too busy rounding up and hounding down and tying to gateposts to ask. Why anyone should choose to keep four wire-haired terriers together was enough to puzzle over. Within ten minutes of their owner driving away in relief, I was laying about me with an empty pail to keep them from tearing one another apart. Hearing the noise, the other dogs began to stir uneasily as if to a battle cry. I put the newcomers in two kennel runs and spoke to them severely. Their names were Pansy, Posy, Primula and Picklepuss. I chose others, more distinctive and far less flattering.

Ben was packing up. Somehow he had accumulated an enormous amount of possessions, and he came downstairs when he heard the noise to see if he could help. We had played a game of Scrabble to settle the question of a haircut, and by using my two Y's in MYSTERY over a treble square in one flash of brilliance, I had won, by what you might call a short haircut. Grudgingly he had let me do it, fearful of the result. But he was delighted because I left it to the tips of his ears where it curled enough to keep him peering with satisfaction in every mirror he passed.

I said, "Just had a card from Adam. He's coming a couple of days before you leave. You'll meet him. I'm glad of that, though I was thinking of giving him your room and now . . ."

Ben said, "*My* room?" as if I'd suggested handing over his birthright.

"Well, yes. I mean, we did redecorate it and put down the Crossword carpet" (a very odd design in bold squares given to us by Hetty when she was having a fitted one put in her waiting-room) "and it's much nicer than the other spares."

"But what about *me*?"

"You're going home, love . . ." It seemed daft to have to remind him when he was even at that moment looking for string to tie up his books on cooking, recording, animal communication (given to him by Hetty) and *Motorway Construction and Development* which he had found in the Library Van when it visited the village and sworn he'd lost so that he could pay for it and keep it.

"But when I come back?"

I'd never thought of him coming back. Much as I knew I'd miss him, Ben belonged with other people in other places. Or so I'd told myself. Now I wasn't so sure. I felt trapped.

"Next summer, perhaps? Lovely," I said uncertainly.

"Christmas holidays." He was puzzled. "I'll be back then. Well, for some of it, anyway."

I couldn't argue. It was too sensitive an issue altogether. Skating over thin ice, I said, "Then we'll give Adam the end room: maybe we'll have time to do it up a bit. There's that old blue carpet we took out of your room – only needs a shampoo; and some tapestry curtains I was going to have in the morning-room . . ."

I had thought of September being a mellow end of things: instead it was merely transition. We were still talking about Adam's arrival when Emily came in with a hobbling hen. She had it tucked under one arm but put it on the table so I could see the limp and suggest treatment. While I was wondering about the lumps between its toes and hoping Hetty would call during the day, she said, "I wrote to Mummy. I've told her I'd like to go to school in the village and spend the holidays at home. Would you mind?"

I was so startled, I let go of Rosemary, the hen, and she fluttered to the floor and escaped, hopping and clucking through the back door.

"Well, no, of course not. We'll have to see what your mother says. But why?"

"Oh, I'm fed up with lessons at home, and I wouldn't want to go to that huge old Comprehensive where everyone would be faster than me in getting around and I'd get teased and everything. The school in the village would be lovely for a year or two, and the bus picking up the other children passes here. Then I thought I'd have to go home *sometimes* but Mummy and Daddy wouldn't be there, except in holidays, so we could spend them together. It would be a bit like boarding-school, only nice." It made a lot of sense – but where did it leave me? I had an awful feeling that I was being taken over and it was something days-off couldn't cure, nor graffiti however philosophical; a tide of other people's planning swooshed me along and I was too tired to either swim with it or turn and make for the shore.

Max Beerbohm once said in a weak moment, "The woman who is kind to dogs has failed to inspire sympathy in men." I wasn't sure I cared, and anyway I inspired nothing at all in anyone at that moment. I was simply taken for granted. Self-pity was my only friend and it was one I could have done well without. It was probably time to assert myself again, I thought: do something positive, redirect my mind into productivity.

On his final visit, when he collected the afghans and relieved me of the haunting responsibility for their future, Ross had stayed to lunch and told me a little about his life. I had told him everything about mine. Well, almost everything, because the fact that my second toe on each foot is longer than the big one, or the way two bones click in my thigh when I run, seemed irrelevant. But if a love affair can be conducted by verbal intimacy and innuendo of the eyes, all of it condensed over a meal and some washing-up, plus an hour with a jolly pig ambling across meadows in the sunshine, then that was what it was. I think we understood in one another something we found it difficult to understand in ourselves, and any further attempt to improve on that might have merely ruined what we had. Ross told me he would be back with the dogs in the spring, if not before, but I had a strong conviction he wouldn't and, in a lot of ways, I wanted it to end right there. But among other things, he said he admired my versatility in effort and ambition, and remembering that, I wondered if now was a good time to strike out in a different direction, try a bit of sculpting, say, or learn how to lay lino and apply it locally. Well, something I hadn't done wasn't that easy to find.

I decided to start in a small way by grilling instead of frying at lunchtime, and burned a pan full of bubble and squeak until the ceiling turned black. Ben sighed and took over. He had practically decided to go in for catering and was preparing to tell his father, who was coming home, and his mother, who was there already getting herself rehabilitated for family life again.

I thought Ben would do very well as a chef, even maitre d'hotel, but in the meantime I wished he wouldn't droop over his plate, scratch his neck with his thumb and yawn across the table giving a complete view of the undigested beans. School meals and a democratic levelling down have done a lot of disservice to the mere onlooker.

Marsha had rung me in the early hours, obviously wide-eyed from a party and unable to calculate that anyone else might be asleep. "So awful, darling," she giggled. "My foot-fancier – such a super hotel, simply overhanging a lake or something very wet: a suite *and* a balcony, quite Noël Coward and just as dated, too, but restful, you know?" I wished I did. I could have done with it. I just stood and yawned and tried to listen. ". . . using his own name and address – well, for credit cards, expense accounts, all that you know – and didn't I have to leave my lovely lacy panties in the bathroom? So didn't they have to go and forward them on to *Mrs* Foot-Fancier – I mean, the *real* one?" She paused for effect. I yawned for the thirteenth time. I wasn't even enjoying the sunrise outside.

"It's not that I grudge her my panties, darling," she went on earnestly. "After all, he bought me lots and lots, but the hotel, as one of their publicity stunts, popped in a sweet little fluffy toy kitten. And more than anything in the world I wanted a kitten for myself. Well, it's not fair. I mean, it was really meant for me because I know the Hotel Manager did rather fancy me, sweetie, and there was even a little note on the collar which said . . ."

"Goodnight, Marsha," I butted in. "I couldn't care a fig." And I went back up to bed and burst into sobs. I cried away all the tears I left unshed for Rover, for the bubble and squeak and for sentimental memories and nostalgia over Ross.

One smack and I'd crack, I thought next morning. Long ago and far away were the hemlines when I fancied myself as Maid Marian, but here and now was the same point of collapse that had closed the sewing-machine. I chalked, in a quavering hand, "WE WILL OVERCOME!" above the top shelf of the dresser where even dear, faithful Toby could never have licked it off. I stood back and looked at it, falling over a stool, lurching about over-tired and irritable, snapping at the phone when it rang.

A Mrs Harris would not be back for her boxer for another two weeks at least. I put on the kettle. No one had collected the enormous Newfoundland, a sleepy creature who snored until the slates rattled. There was never a reply from the owner's number and Directory Enquiries coolly informed me it was a spare line and no one ever would. I had to face the unwelcome fact that I was being dumped. The odd cairn or occasional small crossbred could usually be found a good home, but who wants eleven stone with bad teeth and temper?

I announced over breakfast that we would have to get on with the painting. Hetty had warned me that Baby would have to go to the Bacon Factory in a week or two or his snout would wreck the entire place. He was a huge and happy pig and twice the gate to his kennel-run had been wrenched off its hinges in one glorious moment of light-hearted abandon to snout a way out. Getting him back presented the ultimate in time, strength, despair, wear and considerable tear, as I could testify from torn jeans, ripped shirt, and a cut hand. Everything seemed to be defeating me. There were very few bookings now the season was nearly over. Just the odd customer from Mrs Sissingtons (and odd they usually were) and the occasional psychiatric nutcase from Hetty to keep my hand in, to stay me with flagons but it was more than flagons I needed. I would think seriously about breeding. Hadn't I once said to Hetty it would occupy me out of season? Yorkshire terriers, perhaps, small and popular. Invest in a really sturdy pair of bitches, perhaps go in for showing from time to time – but the old enthusiasm was missing somehow.

We dragged the ladders into the hall and worked all morning on the walls and doors. Emily and Ben enjoyed every moment. I wished I could. Emily was very good on the tiddley bits which Ben and I smudged. Her magnifying spectacles and a loving regard for detail had already found themselves invaluable in completing the altar cloth, and I had also given her an old box of pastels when I found how amazingly good she was at sketching the animals. Ben was already encouraging her into business, prepared to mount the work she did, frame and sell it to owners, along with his Mock Doggy-Chox.

"TODAY IS THE FIRST DAY OF THE REST OF YOUR LIFE" wa

beginning to wear a bit thin across the larder door. Fighting off tears of a rising depression, I bravely changed the R in REST to a B. It was so easy to do and so difficult to believe. I dredged up old Smile No. 14 – "For Valour", I call it. Not a pretty sight.

"Let's get the hall finished and start on Adam's room," I suggested after lunch and a walk with the dogs. Ben turned on Radio 1 and together we got the long ladder up on the staircase, wedged it safely between the banisters, and I crept slowly to the top so I could just about reach the place where the ceiling took over. My brush was tied to an old broomstick used for steering Baby. Outside the wind was coming in off the sea, bringing rain. It spattered the window as if drumming bored fingers on a sensitive pulse. Ben was doing the inside of the front door, Emily was edging the dado, and Tony Blackburn was doing his nut. I was hating the height but apart from an occasional wobble, I was doing fairly well. When it was finished, I promised myself, I would creep into bed and sleep for a few hours. Or days, or ever . . .

And then the bell went outside the front door. "Open it, Ben," I called hoping it was the Newfoundland's owner. In too much of a hurry I began the perilous descent. Even so, if it hadn't been for Baby on a plunge through the hall chasing Sidney the fox, I would never have caught my bare foot in the bottom rung and fallen, over and over, thudding and thumping, banging and bruising, until my head hit the newel post at the bottom. I just managed to hear my husband saying, "Christmas! whatever is she doing *now*?" before passing out cold.

Emily helped bring in the breakfast tray, and the first thing I noticed was the *teapot*. It was symbolic. Tears crept under my lids because, for the first time, the house was a home. I could hear the vacuum purring gently downstairs. The window was open and through the balcony doors I could see Rajah and Rosie idling away the time with a rabbit's leg. The corgis were barking. I remembered the way they had been barking all day yesterday – was it yesterday? I remembered the fall and the upturned paint. There was a big important bit missing somewhere, like the smile in a jigsaw of the Mona Lisa. I tried to find it. I *had* to find it . . .

I found it. I tried to sit up, and couldn't.

"Not *you*?" I said to my husband.

"Who else walks into your bedroom with breakfast these days?"

He sat down and picked up my hand. It smelled of turps. I let tears run slowly into the pillow. I was glad they were there. It emphasised the point I'd been trying to make behind the barrier of words all those weeks. Maybe it takes a bang on the head to shake up emotions and recognise the right order. Because wasn't this quite near what I had really longed for so often? And here we were, with soft music and sunshine to boot. The music was pop on the radio and there was a hint of rain outside, but the rest was there. I closed my eyes again.

"Hey!" he cried, alarmed at what might lead to a faint or something equally unmanageable, "everything's under control, but you'll have to give me a few leads." ("They're on a peg in the porch," I muttered.) "I mean about fees and fuses and where you keep the runny honey. But I never felt more like a challenge in my life so I'm taking over." He sounded delighted. "If there's anything worse than doing too much as you have, it's not doing much at all, like me. Ben and Em and I are getting thoroughly organised. Oliver's bringing a friend to finish the decorating. Baby *likes* being next to the battling terriers, and he hasn't even tried to get out. The turtle nearly drowned so we've got it in the copper preserving pan." I opened my mouth to protest and then shut it again. It was a very small turtle. "Sidney has the play-pen in the conservatory. I'm not saying you're not needed but it *is* my turn to feel useful, you know And this egg's just four minutes. The toast won't keep, either."

He helped me sit up. I thought what a fright I must look. He was tanned and smelled faintly of sea water. Pain shot through my head my shoulders, my leg. "Oooh!" I groaned.

"Hetty says nothing's broken but she's sending up her own doctor to check, just in case."

"Hetty?" How had Hetty come into it? But didn't Hetty *alway* come into it? Every drama and trauma seemed to fetch her out o the woodwork like a busy worm. No, that was unfair. Out of ever unexpected parcel, like the perfect present. What would I have don without Hetty? She had apparently arrived while they were rescu ing me from the pool of paint.

"Isn't she terrific?" said Pa.

I nodded. The tea from my old pot was soothing, quite differer from the graceful Indian in the coffee-container. More stimulating yet comforting too. Hetty had cleaned me up, got me to bed and or ganised the disaster area in the hall. Mild concussion and bruising she said.

"No small suspect fractures?" I said, teasing a little. He blushed

"Actually," he admitted, "it was more that I didn't feel wanted a home. I could tell I'd only be in the way. It seemed more sense to g all the tests and things finished with, convalescence over and m ankle all right so I wouldn't be a nuisance." Is that how I had ma it sound? But of course none of it mattered any more. We didn't need reasons, excuses or explanations and anyway he was probably right. Nobody has to pretend in a real relationship. The only true bond between lovers is freedom.

"I'm getting up when I've finished this," I said, not meaning a word of it. Ben had cut the crusts off the toast, turned the butter into small thistles, added primulas in a circular holder round my eggcup. I didn't want to eat but more than anything in the world I seemed to have needed that tray. Tears drenched the marmalade. "It's nothing," I said, wiping them with the pink napkin, "just emotion and what you've all done for me." I sniffed. "Why didn't you say you were coming home?"

"I wanted to surprise you."

"And check on the christening spoon."

"Maybe. But I think it was more because I missed you so much."

"Not before, though." I was fishing, of course.

"All the time." Well, so had I really. "I just felt unequal somehow."

"Unequal to what?"

"All the activity." But what activity? It was so peaceful here. Then I heard it – barking, braying, honking: radio, laughter – living. A background so familiar it had long ago merged for me into being and breathing. "Give the egg to Mattie and the bread to the birds. I can't, honestly. But I don't want Ben and Emily to know."

I lay back and closed my eyes. I stopped lining up the kennels with the apples, herbs, tomatoes and the lilies of yesteryear. "Is there anywhere in the world where Rates don't rear their ugly head?"

"Funny," he said eagerly, moving the tray, sitting on the bed, kissing me, "but I do happen to have an ad. here about a small offshore island some place where actual nationality is still a bit in doubt and it's let to tenants prepared to produce hemp and kelp." It sounded like a double act, not a very good one.

He began to study the cutting and a sheaf of letters attached.

"No," I said firmly, and I looked out across the balcony to the Motorway. For a reason I would probably be able to articulate the next day, I didn't want to travel along it to offshore islands, city lights or the end of the rainbow. Not now. Possibly not ever. I just wanted to stay here, where I was, and watch everyone else pelting past trying to find the crock of gold.

Because for me, now, the magic of the Motorway ended where we were.